K. A. HESSE:

GRADED ARITHMETIC PRACTICE

BOOK THREE
Teacher's Edition

Longman

CONTENTS OF TEACHER'S BOOK

FOREWORD

As its title implies, this course makes no claim to replace the teacher, nor does it seek to introduce new concepts in the teaching of mathematics. But just as the highly skilled craftsman requires the finest of tools, so does the mathematics teacher require sets of exercises ready at hand to make effective the skill he has applied to his teaching. The application of these exercises will depend on the material to be dealt with, and since the material is human and of diverse qualities and characteristics only the teacher can decide in what manner and for how long the application should be made.

Once a topic or process has been taught the pupil can be directed to the appropriate page in this book, where the right type of exercise, carefully prepared and graded both in the difficulty of process and of computation, will encourage the pupil as he combines development of speed with accuracy. At each step the amount of practice provided is in relation to the degree of difficulty, so that the necessary facility with each particular topic is assured. To avoid the tendency of most people to be extravagant in the use of some digits and numbers to the partial exclusion of others, the use of number combinations has been carefully checked. Groups of these (*Speed Practice*) head many of the pages, and it is left to the teacher to decide how much practice is necessary and how that practice shall be undertaken.

For the quicker, progressive pupil the material is there, boldly set out in a simple and straightforward manner, so that the teacher's guidance which is required will be at a minimum. Thus the teacher is enabled to give extra time to the needs of slower pupils, and to concentrate more on the teaching of the *application* of mathematics to the pupils' needs and interests.

The planning of the book attempts to prevent long lapses of time between commencing a rule or process and returning to extend it. This avoids staleness, allows for maturing to take place, allows number combinations and tables to be dealt with in easily assimilated groups, giving opportunity for more preparation if necessary, according to the needs of the pupil, and allows for integration of topics wherever possible. As in the previous books the mathematical terms appropriate to each process have been consolidated and extended. At convenient points throughout the book Revision pages are provided. To further assist the teacher notes are provided at the bottom of pages, together with references to further notes for blackboard work arranged on pages 79–82.

NUMBER COMBINATIONS AND BASIC TABLE FACTS

Success in arithmetic depends upon complete mastery of number combinations and basic table facts as much as on any other factor. Tables in Addition and Subtraction are in need of similar treatment to those in Multiplication and Division and all must be kept in their true perspective by teachers. Too many are apt to view the learning of tables from the adult's attitude rather than from that of the pupil. Few children find repetition a drudgery unless the lack of enthusiasm of the teacher inculcates that same attitude into the pupils, or the degree of difficulty is wrong. In order to deal efficiently with learning a new process or application, all the number facts to be used should be completely mastered prior to the teaching of that process. Only in this way can the pupil concentrate on the one difficulty.

Most arithmetic lessons in any Junior School should include practice in tables, both orally and in writing, but it is not enough to expect the child to commit the numbers facts to memory. It is important that the pupil develops a number sense and a ready facility in mental reckoning. This involves more than working from the concrete to the abstract and in practical application, it involves an awareness of relationships.

The pupil must not only realise and know that, for example,

$8 + 5 = 13, \quad 5 + 8 = 13, \quad 13 - 8 = 5, \quad 13 - 5 = 8$

but at this stage the development should be continued so that there is a ready transference to

$8 + 5 = 13, \quad 18 + 5 = 23, \quad 38 + 5 = 43,$ etc.,

$13 - 8 = 5, \quad 23 - 8 = 15, \quad 63 - 8 = 55,$ etc.

Most pages in this book carry a group of number combinations or basic table facts set out for speed practice, but it is important that oral work is carried out by the teacher in order to adjust the degree of difficulty to the ability of the pupils. Owing to economic use of space and the varying needs of pupils, only representative examples can be included in these groups. Here is one way in which these groups may be treated after the necessary oral build-up has taken place. First, the pupil marks off three double pages in an exercise book as 1, 2 and 3. Then, on his first page, he works through the number facts contained in any one group at his best speed and leaves them without marking. He repeats the process on page 2, and finally repeats it on page 3, but this time they are marked. The child is thus challenging himself rather than his fellows and at the same time speeding up the mental process. With pupils of average ability it is advisable to let them work again at frequent intervals some of the groups they have already dealt with.

If the pupil is led to understand that this practice is for his benefit, and not for the teacher to discover what he has not learned; that he is competing against himself and not being compared with his fellows; that he is working on three separate pages in order to help against temptation, and not because he is mistrusted, then the teacher is likely to have the full co-operation of the pupil in a happy and industrious atmosphere. Depending upon the pupil's success with these groups the teacher will be able to judge to what degree, if any, the group must be amplified and how much more practice the pupil should need.

K.A. HESSE:

GRADED ARITHMETIC PRACTICE

BOOK THREE

LONGMAN GROUP LIMITED
London

Associated companies, branches and represenatives throughout the world

© K. A. Hesse 1962
Decimal and Metric Edition © Longman Group Ltd 1970

All rights reserved. No part of this publication may be reproduced, stored in a retrieval system, or transmitted in any form or by any means, electronic, mechanical, photocopying, recording, or otherwise, without the prior permission of the Copyright owner.

First published 1962
Decimal and Metric edition first published 1970
Fourth impression 1974

Pupils' edition ISBN 0 582 18169 0
Teachers' edition ISBN 0 582 18170 4

Printed in Hong Kong by
Commonwealth Printing Press Ltd

Work across the page

Write answers only:

A	8p−5p=3p	7p+3p=10p	4p+7p=11p	5p+ 6p=11p
B	7p−4p=3p	9p−6p= 3p	11p−5p= 6p	13p− 8p= 5p
C	15p−6p=9p	9p+7p=16p	8p+9p=17p	8p+10p=18p
D	3p×3 =9p	4p×5 =20p	7p×4 =28p	6p×5 =30p
E	16p÷4 =4p	21p÷7 = 3p	30p÷6 = 5p	42p÷7 = 6p
F	$\frac{1}{2}$ of 12 g=6g	$\frac{1}{2}$ of 20 cm=10 cm	$\frac{1}{3}$ of 15 mm=5mm	$\frac{2}{3}$ of 18 mm=12 mm
G	$\frac{1}{2}$ of 100=50	$\frac{1}{2}$ of £1=£0·50 (50p)	$\frac{1}{4}$ of £1=£0·25 (25p)	$\frac{1}{2}$ of 50p=25p
H	6 cm×7=42 cm	8 cm×8=64 cm	7 cm×9=63 cm	9 cm×8=72 cm
I	27 kg÷9=3 kg	36 kg÷12=3 kg	72 m÷9=8 m	84 hr.÷7=12 hr.
J	48 hr.÷6=8 hr.	60 hr.÷12=5 hr.	96 m÷12=8 m	63 m÷9=7 m

K	30 minutes	= $\frac{1}{2}$ hour	30 seconds	= $\frac{1}{2}$ minute
L	$1\frac{1}{2}$ minutes	= 90 seconds	3 weeks	= 21 days
M	12 hours	= $\frac{1}{2}$ day	$\frac{1}{2}$ kilogramme	= 500 grammes
N	$\frac{1}{2}$ kilometre	= 500 metres	250 millilitres	= $\frac{1}{4}$ litre
O	$\frac{1}{2}$ centimetre	= 5 millimetres	$\frac{1}{2}$ metre	= 50 centimetres
P	50 centimetres	= $\frac{1}{2}$ metre	$\frac{1}{2}$ metre	= 500 millimetres
Q	4 tens	= 8 fives	1 fifty	= 10 fives
R	2 tens	= 10 twos	£3	= 6 fifties
S	14 twos	= 2 tens + 4 twos	9 fives	= 4 tens + 1 five
T	6 tens	= 12 fives	£2	= 40 fives
U	100 millilitres	= $\frac{1}{10}$ (0·1) litre	2 litres	= 2000 millilitres
V	10 fifties	= 5 pounds	7 cm 8 mm	= 78 millimetres

This page with the three which follow are to prepare the pupil for taking the Check page on p. 5 to determine the pupil's readiness to proceed with this book. All errors should be examined to determine if they are factual or computational.

REVISION OF NUMBER

Work across the page

State in figures the value of the figure six in each of these numbers:

A	1 607	600	2 786	6	6 400	6000	167	60	3 060	60
B	4·36	0·06	16·04	6	50·6	0·6	0·68	0·6	5·06	0·06

Write in words

C	3 094	Three thousand and ninety four	17·6	Seventeen point six
D	24·65	Twenty four point six five	4·08	Four point nought eight
E	25 809	Twenty five thousand eight hundred and nine		

Write as decimals

F	five units, three tenths and two hundredths	5·32
G	eight point nought seven	8·07

Add (+)

H

32	67	43	957	496	589
14	85	60	147	778	437
56	54	98	806	609	984
102	206	201	1910	1883	2010

Subtract (−)

I

74	50	87	324	600	538
− 34	− 26	− 39	− 108	− 537	− 199
40	24	48	216	63	339

Multiply (×)

J

52	69	87	509	967	345
× 4	× 3	× 6	× 7	× 9	× 12
208	207	522	3563	8703	4140

Divide (÷)

K

203	60r3	75	1001r1	196
3)609	5)303	8)600	9)9010	11)2156

REVISION OF LENGTH

Measure these lines, giving the answer first in millimetres and then in centimetres and millimetres

A ________ 16 mm; 1 cm 6 mm ____________ 24 mm; 2 cm 4 mm

B ____________________ 38 mm; 3 cm 8 mm ______ 12 mm; 1 cm 2 mm

C ____ 90 mm; 9 cm

State which measurement you would use, kilometres, metres or millimetres to measure each of these lengths

D The length of a match mm — the thickness of a pencil mm

E The length of a river km — the length of a street m

F The distance between lamp-posts m — the distance between cities km

G A journey to the seaside km — the length of a garden m

Complete

H $\frac{1}{2}$ km = 500 metres — 2 km = 2 000 metres — $\frac{1}{2}$ m = 50 centimetres

I 25 cm = $\frac{1}{4}$ metre — 5 mm = $\frac{1}{2}$ cm — 200 cm = 2 metres

J $\frac{1}{5}$ km = 200 metres — $\frac{2}{5}$ km = 400 metres — $\frac{2}{5}$ m = 40 centimetres

K $\frac{1}{5}$ cm = 2 mm — 4 mm = $\frac{2}{5}$ cm — $\frac{1}{2}$ cm = 5 millimetres

Write the first answer as a fraction and the second as a decimal

L 1 mm = $\frac{1}{10}$ cm or 0·1 cm — 3 mm = $\frac{3}{10}$ cm or 0·3 cm

M 6 mm = $\frac{6}{10}$ cm or 0·6 cm — 9 mm = $\frac{9}{10}$ cm or 0·9 cm

N 11 mm = $1\frac{1}{10}$ cm or 1·1 cm — 17 mm = $1\frac{7}{10}$ cm or 1·7 cm

O 29 mm = $2\frac{9}{10}$ cm or 2·9 cm — 53 mm = $5\frac{3}{10}$ cm or 5·3 cm

Write in columns and add

P 2·3 cm + 1·6 cm + 2·2 cm 6·1 cm — 3·1 cm + 0·8 cm + 4·3 cm 8·2 cm

Q 1·4 km + 4·5 km + 3·4 km 9·3 km — 0·5 m + 3·3 m + 5·7 m 9·5 m

Write in columns and subtract

R 6·7 mm − 3·4 mm 3·3 mm — 7·2 cm − 4·8 cm 2·4 cm — 5·3 km − 0·8 km 4·5 km

S 20·2 m − 8·4 m 11·8 m — 20 km − 7·6 km 12·4 km — 0·81 m − 0·57 m 0·24 m

REVISION OF MONEY

Write what you should add to each of these amounts to equal 2 tens

A 3 fives, a two and a one — a two; 2 fives, 2 twos and a one — a five

B 1 five, 4 twos and 3 ones — two twos; 3 fives, a one and 2 halves — a two and a one

Write what change you should receive from a fifty after paying

C 3 tens, a five and a two — 13p; 2 tens, 2 fives and 6 ones — 14p

D 4 tens, a five and 2 twos — 1p; 1 ten, 7 fives and 2 twos — 1p

Complete

E $4\frac{1}{2}p - 2\frac{1}{2}p = 2p$ $2\frac{1}{2}p + 1\frac{1}{2}p = 4p$ $3p - 1\frac{1}{2}p = 1\frac{1}{2}p$ $7p - 5\frac{1}{2}p = 1\frac{1}{2}p$

Write as pence

F £1·26 = 126p £3·70 = 370p £0·94 = 94p £0·90$\frac{1}{2}$ = 90$\frac{1}{2}$p

Write as pounds

G 256p = £2·56 140p = £1·40 83p = £0·83 10$\frac{1}{2}$p = £0·10$\frac{1}{2}$

Write as figures

H five pounds sixty-four £5·64 thirty pounds eight £30·08

Add (+)

I

12$\frac{1}{2}$p	23$\frac{1}{2}$p	14$\frac{1}{2}$p	32$\frac{1}{2}$p	14$\frac{1}{2}$p	25$\frac{1}{2}$p
25$\frac{1}{2}$p	8$\frac{1}{2}$p	40$\frac{1}{2}$p	20 p	37 p	9$\frac{1}{2}$p
14$\frac{1}{2}$p	20$\frac{1}{2}$p	19 p	19$\frac{1}{2}$p	8$\frac{1}{2}$p	30$\frac{1}{2}$p
52$\frac{1}{2}$p	52$\frac{1}{2}$p	74 p	72 p	60 p	65$\frac{1}{2}$p

J

£2·13	£4·25	£2·47	£0·37$\frac{1}{2}$	£23·43	£4·06$\frac{1}{2}$
1·45	0·63	0·62	4·06$\frac{1}{2}$	7·08	0·87
2·54	3·42	4·73	0·25$\frac{1}{2}$	15·81	0·09$\frac{1}{2}$
£6·12	£8·30	£7·82	£4·69$\frac{1}{2}$	£46·32	£5·03

Subtract (−)

K

82$\frac{1}{2}$p	40$\frac{1}{2}$p	69 p	72 p	93 p	80 p
− 57$\frac{1}{2}$p	− 27 p	− 35$\frac{1}{2}$p	− 38$\frac{1}{2}$p	− 79$\frac{1}{2}$p	− 39$\frac{1}{2}$p
25 p	13$\frac{1}{2}$p	33$\frac{1}{2}$p	33$\frac{1}{2}$p	13$\frac{1}{2}$p	40$\frac{1}{2}$p

L

£4·29	£5·03	£0·70	£0·82$\frac{1}{2}$	£0·70	£2
− 2·70	− 3·07	− 0·53	− 0·67	− 0·36$\frac{1}{2}$	− 0·60$\frac{1}{2}$
£1·59	£1·96	£0·17	£0·15$\frac{1}{2}$	£0·33$\frac{1}{2}$	£1·39$\frac{1}{2}$

PROGRESS CHECK PAGE

Add (+)

A

215	387	609
387	260	84
609	53	307
1211	700	1000

Subtract (−)

B

520	813	706
−413	−790	−98
107	23	608

Multiply (×)

C

347	975	286
× 5	× 8	× 12
1735	7800	3432

Divide (÷)

D

50r4	100r1	19r1
6)304	9)901	11)210

Write as centimetres and millimetres

E 1·4cm 1cm4mm 1·7cm 1cm7mm 3·0cm 3cm $4\frac{1}{2}$cm 4cm5mm

Write as centimetres

F 1cm2mm 1·2cm 4cm9mm 4·9cm 26mm 2·6cm 35mm 3·5cm

Write in columns and add

G 3·7cm+0·5cm+6·6cm 10·8cm 4cm+5·8cm+0·7cm 10·5cm

Write in columns and subtract

H 4·7cm−1·4cm 3·3cm 3·5cm−0·8cm 2·7cm 10cm−5·7cm 4·3cm

Write as pence

I £1·32 132p £1·06 106p £0·70 70p £0·17$\frac{1}{2}$ 17$\frac{1}{2}$p £0·08$\frac{1}{2}$ 8$\frac{1}{2}$p

Write as pounds

J 43p £0·43 9p £0·09 240p £2·40 60$\frac{1}{2}$p £0·60$\frac{1}{2}$ 102$\frac{1}{2}$p £1·02$\frac{1}{2}$

Write in columns and add

K £2·13+£1·07+£3·92 £7·12 £3·64+£1·80$\frac{1}{2}$+£0·09$\frac{1}{2}$ £5·54

Write in columns and subtract

L £27·36−£9·44 £17·92 £7·10−£3·25 £3·85 £2·40−£0·48$\frac{1}{2}$ £1·91$\frac{1}{2}$

Should any pupil fail to get correct one sum in any lettered group, that pupil should be referred to the appropriate "Four Rules" book.

EXTENDING NUMBER COMBINATIONS

Work across the page

Add (+)

A	9+3= 12	2+8= 10	4+5= 9	3+7= 10	8+0= 8
B	6+4= 10	2+9= 11	5+6= 11	9+4= 13	6+7= 13
C	9+5= 14	6+9= 15	8+7= 15	7+9= 16	8+9= 17
D	11+2= 13	12+5= 17	13+4= 17	12+8= 20	14+5= 19
E	15+6= 21	17+3= 20	12+9= 21	14+7= 21	16+8= 24
F	17+8= 25	19+6= 25	18+7= 25	19+9= 28	20+6= 26
G	21+3= 24	23+5= 28	22+8= 30	24+5= 29	26+4= 30
H	23+7= 30	25+6= 31	24+7= 31	23+8= 31	25+7= 32
I	26+5= 31	23+9= 32	25+8= 33	22+9= 31	19+8= 27
J	25+9= 34	26+8= 34	24+9= 33	28+5= 33	27+6= 33

Subtract (−)

K	5− 3= 2	6−2= 4	4− 4= 0	7− 5= 2	6−3= 3
L	7− 4= 3	8−5= 3	5− 0= 5	9− 2= 7	8−6= 2
M	8− 3= 5	9−6= 3	9− 4= 5	8− 7= 1	9−3= 6
N	11− 8= 3	12−9= 3	11− 3= 8	9− 5= 4	12−4= 8
O	12− 5= 7	13−4= 9	13− 9= 4	14− 5= 9	11−7= 4
P	13− 5= 8	12−7= 5	14− 6= 8	13− 6= 7	12−8= 4
Q	14− 8= 6	13−7= 6	14− 7= 7	13− 8= 5	15−6= 9
R	15− 9= 6	14−9= 5	15− 7= 8	15− 8= 7	16−7= 9
S	17− 8= 9	16−8= 8	16−10= 6	17−10= 7	11−9= 2
T	18−10= 8	17−9= 8	18− 9= 9	19−10= 9	16−9= 7

Complete

U	2+3=12− 7	5+2=11− 4	3+6=16− 7
V	13−4=15− 6	14−6=17− 9	16−9= 5+ 2
W	15−7= 2+ 6	17−9=18− 10	3+5=13− 5

Pupils of average ability should be able to achieve 45 correct answers in 6 minutes for group **A–J** and group **K–T**.

SPEED PRACTICE

Add (+)

A	19+1=20	19+0=19	20+1=21	19+2=21	21+1=22
B	20+2=22	19+3=22	22+1=23	21+2=23	20+3=23
C	19+4=23	23+1=24	23+3=26	21+3=24	20+4=24
D	19+5=24	21+4=25	22+2=24	22+3=25	20+5=25
E	22+4=26	19+6=25	20+6=26	21+5=26	24+1=25
F	23+2=25	19+7=26	19+8=27	20+7=27	21+6=27
G	24+0=24	24+2=26	25+0=25	25+1=26	24+3=27
H	23+4=27	19+9=28	20+8=28	20+9=29	22+5=27
I	19+0=19	21+7=28	21+8=29	22+6=28	22+7=29

J

580	368	579	698	854	479	658
176	477	98	639	979	908	99
68	199	378	708	799	679	876
824	1044	1055	2045	2632	2066	1633

K

124	231	400	352	435	265	354
233	106	251	375	464	373	478
115	412	130	284	943	97	807
625	504	219	308	375	508	693
1097	1253	1000	1319	2217	1243	2332

L

202	342	465	375	489	378	508
734	685	256	136	705	687	399
686	759	887	908	389	450	776
855	486	549	697	990	879	588
2477	2272	2157	2116	2573	2394	2271

M

177	63	558	1040	1764	2653
324	697	41	2607	2055	1097
577	48	89	1098	2979	3804
989	769	689	3899	1889	1078
2067	1577	1377	8644	8687	8632

Extends number to four-row addition.

Subtract (−)

A	5 − 3 = 2	7 − 4 = 3	6 − 2 = 4	8 − 3 = 5	9 − 3 = 6
B	9 − 5 = 4	4 − 4 = 0	9 − 6 = 3	7 − 5 = 2	8 − 6 = 2
C	10 − 7 = 3	11 − 5 = 6	8 − 5 = 3	11 − 4 = 7	11 − 8 = 3
D	12 − 10 = 2	12 − 4 = 8	13 − 4 = 9	13 − 9 = 4	14 − 5 = 9
E	12 − 5 = 7	13 − 5 = 8	12 − 7 = 5	13 − 6 = 7	13 − 7 = 6
F	12 − 8 = 4	13 − 8 = 5	14 − 6 = 8	14 − 8 = 6	14 − 7 = 7
G	15 − 6 = 9	15 − 9 = 6	14 − 9 = 5	15 − 7 = 8	15 − 8 = 7
H	16 − 7 = 9	17 − 8 = 9	10 − 10 = 0	11 − 10 = 1	13 − 10 = 3
I	16 − 8 = 8	16 − 10 = 6	14 − 10 = 4	15 − 10 = 5	16 − 9 = 7
J	17 − 9 = 8	18 − 10 = 8	17 − 10 = 7	19 − 10 = 9	18 − 9 = 9

Subtract (−)

K	326 − 218 = 108	507 − 109 = 398	600 − 290 = 310	4103 − 1780 = 2323	7864 − 5097 = 2767
L	6476 − 3278 = 3198	4527 − 1898 = 2629	3055 − 1299 = 1756	4706 − 1809 = 2897	3767 − 1999 = 1768
M	3393 − 595 = 2798	3604 − 2976 = 628	5003 − 957 = 4046	7542 − 6668 = 874	1043 − 978 = 65
N	1356 − 977 = 379	7000 − 991 = 6009	5076 − 1078 = 3998	6043 − 989 = 5054	8008 − 7009 = 999
O	1005 − 909 = 96	2006 − 1099 = 907	4007 − 3909 = 98	8000 − 7995 = 5	1870 − 999 = 871

Extends subtraction to four columns.

ADDITION and SUBTRACTION of NUMBER

Write answers only

A What is the total of eleven, nine and twelve? 32

B What will be the new total if 73 is increased by nine? 82

C Subtract nine apples from sixteen apples. 7 apples

D Reduce the sum of twelve and eight by nine. 11

E Find the difference between twenty-one and twelve. 9

F How many fowls are there altogether if there are 12 hens in one crate, 8 in another and 9 in another? 29 hens

G How many pencils are there in a box if 23 of the pencils are blue and 9 are red? 32 pencils

H If there are 17 blue pencils and eight red pencils, how many must I add to the red ones to make as many as there are blue? 9 red pencils

I What number must be added to twelve cakes to make a total of twenty cakes? 8

Work out these sums

J What is the total of 364, 708, 450 and 678? 2 200

K Increase seven-hundred-and-sixty-eight by nine-hundred-and-thirty-four. 1 702

L Find the difference between three-hundred-and-sixty-two and one-hundred-and-sixty-seven. 195

M What must be added to four-hundred-and-thirty-four to make six-hundred-and-twenty-four? 190

N How many more girls than boys are there in a school of two-hundred-and-eighty-three boys and three-hundred-and-twenty-one girls? 38

O How many pupils are there in a school of one-hundred-and-eighty-nine girls and two-hundred-and-eleven boys? 400

P By how many chickens can three-hundred-and-seventy-six be increased to make five-hundred chickens? 124

Q What is the total when a farmer increases his flock of two-hundred-and-fifty-seven sheep by ninety-four sheep? 351 sheep

REVISION of TIME, MEASURING and FRACTIONS

Write the time on these clocks in two ways

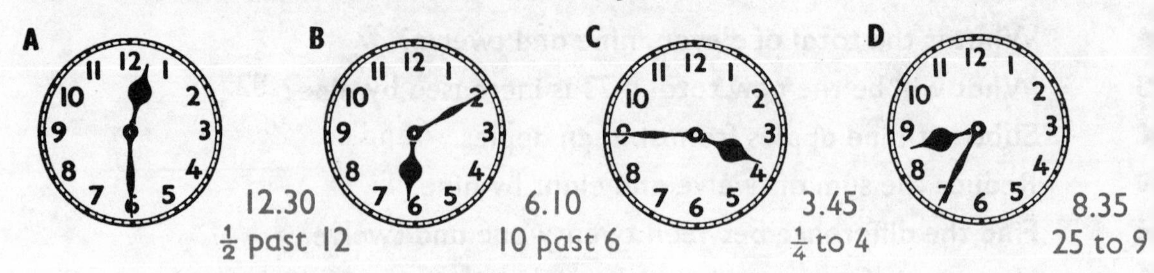

Write the time in figures if

E Clock B was one hour fast. 5.10 Clock C was one hour fast. 2.45

F Clock A was one hour slow. 1.30 Clock D was one hour slow. 9.35

Write answers only

G	$\frac{1}{2}$ of 4 cakes	$=$2 cakes	$\frac{1}{4}$ of 12 sweets	$=$3 sweets
H	$\frac{1}{2}$ of 11p	$=5\frac{1}{2}$p	$\frac{1}{4}$ of 20 cm	$=$5 cm
I	$\frac{1}{4}$ of 6p	$=1\frac{1}{2}$p	$\frac{1}{3}$ of 6p	$=$2p
J	$\frac{1}{3}$ of 12 books	$=$4 books	$\frac{2}{3}$ of 12 books	$=$8 books
K	$\frac{2}{3}$ of 15 cm	$=$10 cm	$\frac{3}{4}$ of 16 apples	$=$12 apples
L	$\frac{3}{4}$ of 20 pens	$=$15 pens	$\frac{2}{3}$ of 24 desks	$=$16 desks

Say how long each line will become if 1·7 cm is added

M __________ 4 cm ____________________ 7·3 cm

N ________________ 5·5 cm ______________ 5·7 cm

Say how long each line will become if 0·6 cm is taken off

O _____________ 2·4 cm _______ 0·9 cm

P __________ 1·6 cm ________________________ 4·7 cm

Complete the following

Q 6 mm $= \frac{1}{2}$ of 12 mm $\quad$ $4 = \frac{1}{3}$ of 12 $\quad$ 5p $= \frac{1}{2}$ of a ten

R 50p $= \frac{1}{2}$ of £1 $\quad$ 25p $= \frac{1}{4}$ of £1 $\quad$ $2\frac{1}{2}$ cm $= \frac{1}{2}$ of 5 cm

Say how much is not shaded on each of these drawings

A 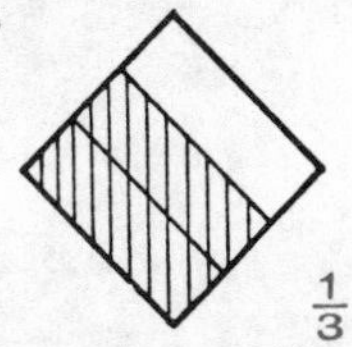 $\frac{1}{3}$ B 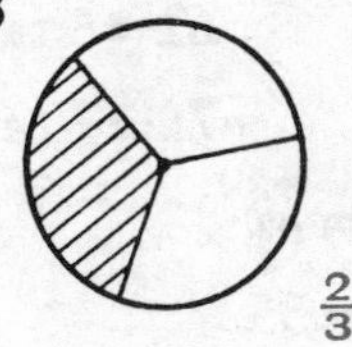 $\frac{2}{3}$ C 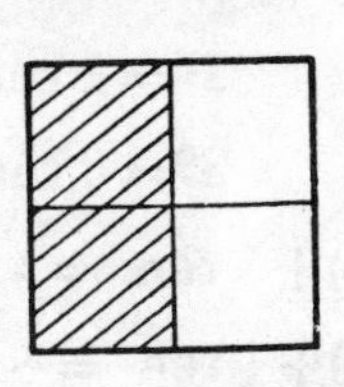 $\frac{1}{2}$ D 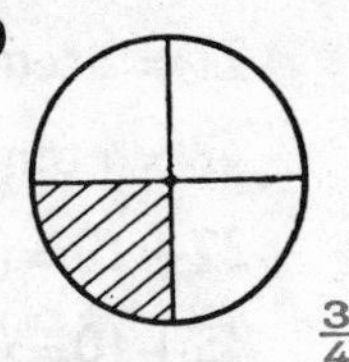 $\frac{3}{4}$

By looking back at the drawings try to find the answers to these sums

E	$\frac{1}{3}+\frac{1}{3}=\frac{2}{3}$	$\frac{2}{3}+\frac{1}{3}=1$	$\frac{1}{4}+\frac{1}{4}=\frac{1}{2}$	$\frac{1}{2}+\frac{1}{2}=1$	$\frac{1}{2}+\frac{1}{4}=\frac{3}{4}$
F	$\frac{2}{3}-\frac{1}{3}=\frac{1}{3}$	$\frac{3}{4}-\frac{1}{4}=\frac{1}{2}$	$\frac{1}{2}-\frac{1}{4}=\frac{1}{4}$	$1-\frac{1}{2}=\frac{1}{2}$	$1-\frac{3}{4}=\frac{1}{4}$
G	$\frac{2}{3}+\frac{2}{3}=1\frac{1}{3}$	$\frac{3}{4}+\frac{1}{4}=1$	$\frac{1}{2}+\frac{3}{4}=1\frac{1}{4}$	$\frac{1}{3}+\frac{2}{3}=1$	$\frac{3}{4}+\frac{1}{2}=1\frac{1}{4}$
H	$\frac{1}{3}-\frac{1}{3}=0$	$\frac{3}{4}-\frac{1}{2}=\frac{1}{4}$	$\frac{2}{3}-\frac{2}{3}=0$	$1-\frac{2}{3}=\frac{1}{3}$	$1\frac{1}{3}-\frac{1}{3}=1$

Complete

I How many halves must be added to $\frac{1}{2}$ to make a whole one? 1

J How many quarters must be added to $\frac{1}{4}$ to make a whole one? 3

K How many thirds must be added to $\frac{1}{3}$ to make a whole one? 2

Say in figures how much of a whole cake is left if we cut away

L	one half	$\frac{1}{2}$	one quarter	$\frac{3}{4}$	one third	$\frac{2}{3}$	two halves	0
M	two quarters	$\frac{1}{2}$	two thirds	$\frac{1}{3}$	three quarters	$\frac{1}{4}$	three thirds	0

Which of these drawings shows by shading $\frac{1}{2}, \frac{1}{4}, \frac{1}{3}, \frac{2}{3}$?

N 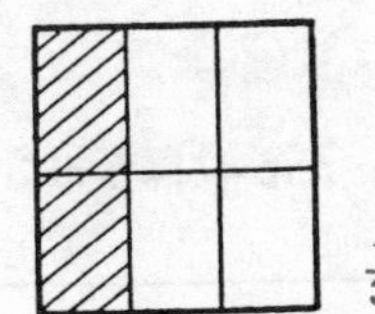 $\frac{1}{3}$ O 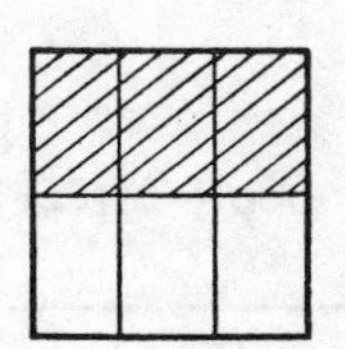 $\frac{1}{2}$ P 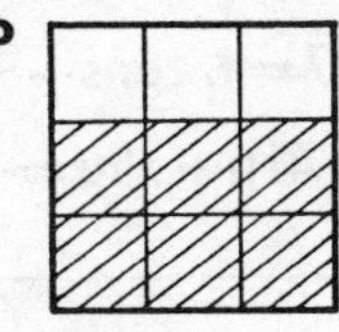 $\frac{2}{3}$ Q 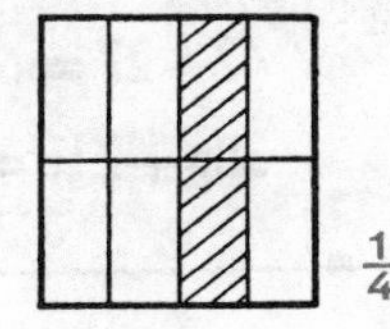 $\frac{1}{4}$

How many halves in

R one apple? 2 two apples? 4 one-and-a-half apples? 3

How many quarters in

S half-an-hour? 2 two hours? 8 one-and-a-half hours? 6

How many thirds in

T one day? 3 three days? 9 one-and-two-thirds days? 5

See notes on page 80.

ADDING LARGE NUMBERS OF PENCE

Work across the page

Complete

A 21 = 2 tens + 1   34 = 3 tens + 4   62 = 6 tens + 2

B 47 = 4 tens + 7   89 = 8 tens + 9   76 = 7 tens + 6

C 32 + 10 = (3 tens + 2) + 1 ten = 4 tens + 2 = 42

D 45 + 10 = (4 tens + 5) + 1 ten = 5 tens + 5 = 55

E 73 + 10 = (7 tens + 3) + 1 ten = 8 tens + 3 = 83

F 34 + 20 = (3 tens + 4) + 2 tens = 5 tens + 4 = 54

G 27 + 20 = (2 tens + 7) + 2 tens = 4 tens + 7 = 47

H 43 + 30 = (4 tens + 3) + 3 tens = 7 tens + 3 = 73

I 23 + 10 = 3 tens + 3 = 33   45 + 20 = 6 tens + 5 = 65

J 34 + 10 = 44   32 + 10 = 42   32 + 20 = 52   44 + 20 = 64   67 + 30 = 97

K 39 + 40 = 79   68 + 30 = 98   56 + 20 = 76   49 + 40 = 89   36 + 40 = 76

L 25p + 10p = 35p   37p + 20p = 57p   63p + 30p = 93p   45p + 20p = 65p

M 48p + 30p = 78p   55p + 40p = 95p   36p + 40p = 76p   77p + 20p = 97p

---

N 34 + 12 = (3 tens + 4) + (1 ten + 2) = 4 tens + 4 + 2 = 46

O 43 + 21 = (4 tens + 3) + (2 tens + 1) = 6 tens + 3 + 1 = 64

P 37 + 21 = 5 tens + 7 + 1 = 5 tens + 8 = 58

Q 55 + 14 = 6 tens + 5 + 4 = 6 tens + 9 = 69

R 42 + 27 = 6 tens + 2 + 7 = 6 tens + 9 = 69

S 38p + 21p = 59p   41p + 35p = 76p   66p + 23p = 89p   75p + 14p = 89p

---

T 36 + 17 = 4 tens + (6 + 7) = 4 tens + (1 ten + 3) = 5 tens + 3 = 53

U 28 + 26 = 4 tens + (8 + 6) = 4 tens + (1 ten + 4) = 5 tens + 4 = 54

V 47 + 23 = 6 tens + (7 + 3) = 6 tens + (1 ten + 0) = 7 tens + 0 = 70

W 69 + 27 = 8 tens + (9 + 7) = 8 tens + (1 ten + 6) = 96

X 28 + 13 = 41   47 + 24 = 71   38 + 36 = 74   69 + 23 = 92   58 + 34 = 92

Y 36p + 26p = 62p   45p + 17p = 62p   68p + 27p = 95p   39p + 25p = 64p

Z 54p + 38p = 92p   28p + 32p = 60p   49p + 31p = 80p   55p + 38p = 93p

Complete

A	23p+20p=43p	78p+20p=98p	42p+30p=72p	67p+30p=97p
B	47p+32p=79p	24p+32p=56p	67p+21p=88p	43p+25p=68p
C	28p+13p=41p	47p+26p=73p	38p+42p=80p	55p+36p=91p
D	59p+26p=85p	35p+47p=82p	69p+27p=96p	48p+45p=93p
E	36p+48p=84p	54p+29p=83p	48p+38p=86p	77p+18p=95p

F 83p+39p=(8 tens+3)+(3 tens+9)=11 tens+12=12 tens+2=122p

G 75p+46p=(7 tens+5)+(4 tens+6)=11 tens+11=12 tens+1=121p

H 67p+68p=(6 tens+7)+(6 tens+8)=12 tens+15=13 tens+5=135p

I 98p+45p=13 tens+13=14 tens+3=143 p=£1·43

J 89p+58p=13 tens+17=14 tens+7=147 p=£1·47

K 67p+73p=13 tens+10=14 tens+0=140 p=£1·40

L 49p+68p=10 tens+17=11 tens+7=117 p=£1·17

M 58p+49p=9 tens+17=10 tens+7=107 p=£1·07

N	86p+25p=111 p=£1·11	87p+25p=112 p=£1·12
O	97p+14p=111 p=£1·11	76p+54p=130 p=£1·30
P	76p+45p=121 p=£1·21	88p+32p=120 p=£1·20
Q	68p+59p=127 p=£1·27	57p+68p=125 p=£1·25
R	87p+37p=124 p=£1·24	96p+48p=144 p=£1·44
S	93p+69p=162 p=£1·62	78p+52p=130 p=£1·30

T	40p+56p= 96p	60p+40p=100p	58p+30p= 88 p=£0·88
U	37p+45p= 82p	26p+67p= 93p	47p+38p= 85 p=£0·85
V	58p+39p= 97p	37p+59p= 96p	76p+24p=100 p=£1
W	67p+35p=102p	48p+67p=115p	83p+27p=110 p=£1·10
X	48p+66p=114p	75p+88p=163p	68p+59p=127 p=£1·27
Y	36p+79p=115p	86p+59p=145p	71p+99p=170 p=£1·70
Z	79p+68p=147p	68p+88p=156p	97p+89p=186 p=£1·86

See notes on page 80.

SUBTRACTING LARGE NUMBERS OF PENCE

A	30−27=27 up to 30=3		40−35=35 up to 40=5	
B	60−53=53 up to 60=7		70−64=64 up to 70=6	
C	80−71=71 up to 80=9		50−43=43 up to 50=7	
D	20p−14p=6p	20p−17p=3p	20p−12p=8p	20p−16p=4p
E	70p−66p=4p	70p−62p=8p	50p−44p=6p	80p−78p=2p
F	80p−74p=6p	90p−83p=7p	90p−85p=5p	60p−52p=8p
G	60p−57p=3p	40p−38p=2p	40p−37p=3p	70p−64p=6p
H	90p−82p=8p	30p−26p=4p	30p−23p=7p	90p−83p=7p

I	50−40=10	50−20=30	50−10=40	50−30=20
J	50−10=40	50−30=20	50−40=10	50−20=30

K 50−38=(38 up to 40) and (40 up to 50)=2 and 10=12

L 50−27=(27 up to 30) and (30 up to 50)=3 and 20=23

M 50−16=(16 up to 20) and (20 up to 50)=4 and 30=34

N 50−12=(12 up to 20) and (20 up to 50)=8 and 30=38

O 50−21=(21 up to 30) and (30 up to 50)=9 and 20=29

P	50−33=7 and 10=17		50−18=2 and 30=32	
Q	50−26=4 and 20=24		50−35=5 and 10=15	
R	50−14=6 and 30=36		50−22=8 and 20=28	
S	50p−40p=10p	50p−39p=11p	50p−37p=13p	50p−32p=18p
T	50p−20p=30p	50p−18p=32p	50p−15p=35p	50p−17p=33p
U	50p−30p=20p	50p−26p=24p	50p−21p=29p	50p−23p=27p
V	50p−10p=40p	50p− 4p=46p	50p−38p=12p	50p−46p= 4p
W	50p−23p=27p	50p−37p=13p	50p−15p=35p	50p−22p=28p

A	19p − 15p = 4p	17p − 8p = 9p	20p − 13p = 7p	19p − 12p = 7p
B	20p − 12p = 8p	20p − 13p = 7p	25p − 22p = 3p	35p − 31p = 4p
C	45p − 42p = 3p	65p − 61p = 4p	95p − 93p = 2p	85p − 84p = 1p
D	50p − 43p = 7p	70p − 67p = 3p	85p − 82p = 3p	80p − 72p = 8p
E	55p − 52p = 3p	60p − 52p = 8p	70p − 63p = 7p	40p − 31p = 9p
F	60p − 54p = 6p	35p − 33p = 2p	90p − 87p = 3p	30p − 26p = 4p

---

G 100 − 78 = (78 up to 80) and (80 up to 100) = and 20 = 22

H 100 − 83 = (83 up to 90) and (90 up to 100) = 7 and 10 = 17

I 100 − 69 = (69 up to 70) and (70 up to 100) = 1 and 30 = 31

J 100 − 45 = (45 up to 50) and (50 up to 100) = 5 and 50 = 55

K 100 − 26 = (26 up to 30) and (30 up to 100) = 4 and 70 = 74

L	100 − 65 = 5 and 30 = 35	100 − 86 = 4 and 10 = 14
M	100 − 37 = 3 and 60 = 63	100 − 29 = 1 and 70 = 71
N	100 − 72 = 8 and 20 = 28	100 − 53 = 7 and 40 = 47
O	100 − 48 = 2 and 50 = 52	100 − 61 = 9 and 30 = 39
P	100 − 64 = 6 and 30 = 36	100 − 36 = 4 and 60 = 64

Q	100p − 92p = 8p	100p − 89p = 11p	100p − 87p = 13p	100p − 83p = 17p
R	100p − 75p = 25p	100p − 72p = 28p	100p − 66p = 34p	100p − 68p = 32p
S	100p − 41p = 59p	100p − 48p = 52p	100p − 57p = 43p	100p − 53p = 47p
T	100p − 29p = 71p	100p − 26p = 74p	100p − 24p = 76p	100p − 25p = 75p
U	100p − 35p = 65p	100p − 38p = 62p	100p − 31p = 69p	100p − 34p = 66p
V	100p − 73p = 27p	100p − 54p = 46p	100p − 85p = 15p	100p − 47p = 53p
W	£1 − 87p = 13p	£1 − 96p = 4p	£1 − 64p = 36p	£1 − 33p = 67p
X	£1 − 59p = 41p	£1 − 42p = 58p	£1 − 26p = 74p	£1 − 72p = 28p

MAKING PAYMENTS

State which of these amounts you could pay for with a 50p coin

A 20p 47p 39p 18p 67p 12p 40p 25p

20p 47p 39p 18p 12p 40p 25p

State which of these amounts you could pay for with 2 tens

B 10p 25p 17p 12p 35p 16p 11p 9p

10p 17p 12p 16p 11p 9p

State which of these amounts you could pay for with 6 tens

C 50p 35p 55p 43p 66p 60p 51p 25p

50p 35p 55p 43p 60p 51p 25p

State which of these amounts you could pay for with 4 tens and a five

D 50p 40p 41p 30p 60p 44p 54p 42p

40p 41p 30p 44p 42p

State the values of three coins that would pay exactly for

E 7p 9p 21p 16p

1 five+2 ones 1 five+2 twos 2 tens+1 one 1 ten+1 five+1 one

F 25p 12p 17p 5p

2 tens+1 five 1 ten+2 ones 2 fives+1 two 1 ten+1 five+1 two 2 twos+1 one

G 70p 60p £1·10 57p

1 fifty+2 tens 1 fifty+2 fives 2 fifties+1 ten 1 fifty+1 five+1 two

State what is the smallest number of coins that would pay exactly for

H 10p 1 15p 2 30p 3 8p 3 11p 2 17p 3 19p 4 25p 3

I 40p 4 55p 2 53p 3 17p 3 65p 3 70p 3 88p 7 33p 5

State what change you should have from 2 tens when paying

J 18p 2p 15p 5p 19p 1p 11p 9p 20p 0 12p 8p 16p 4p 13p 7p

State what change you should have from 3 tens when paying

K 28p 2p 21p 9p 25p 5p 22p 8p 27p 3p 23p 7p 26p 4p 24p 6p

State what change you should have from 4 tens when paying

L 32p 8p 38p 2p 36p 4p 40p 0 33p 7p 35p 5p 37p 3p 31p 9p

State what change you should have from a fifty when paying

M 47p 3p 3p 47p 40p 10p 26p 24p 5p 45p 36p 14p 12p 38p 24p 26p

N 15p 35p 50p 0 23p 27p 42p 8p 34p 16p 17p 33p 25p 25p 18p 32p

State what change you should have from £1 when paying

A	90p 10p	72p 28p	44p 56p	57p 43p	33p 67p	59p 41p	46p 54p	23p 77p
B	41p 59p	38p 62p	66p 34p	85p 15p	27p 73p	16p 84p	34p 66p	65p 35p

State what change you should have from £2 when paying

C	£1·70 30p	£1·50 50p	£1·65 35p	£1·28 72p	£1·93 7p	£1·17 83p
D	£1·46 54p	£1·81 19p	£1·34 66p	£1·60 40p	£1·32 68p	£1·61 39p

---

Complete

E	26p+13p=39p	37p+14p=51p	58p+21p=79p	47p+25p=72p
F	53p+18p=71p	66p+27p=93p	45p+38p=83p	64p+29p=93p
G	37p+46p=83p	29p+36p=65p	76p+19p=95p	58p+38p=96p
H	66p+34p=£1	96p+16p=£1·12	87p+36p=£1·23	63p+59p=£1·22
I	72p+48p=£1·20	57p+59p=£1·16	66p+68p=£1·34	74p+67p=£1·41
J	55p+76p=£1·31	68p+77p=£1·45	49p+87p=£1·36	57p+89p=£1·46

Change to pence

K	£0·46 46p	£1·07 107p	£0·70 70p	£1·23 123p	£1·50 150p	£2·03 203p
L	£1·02 102p	£0·80 80p	£0·08 8p	£0·05 5p	£0·70 70p	£0·09 9p

Change to pounds

M	143p £1·43	106p £1·06	130p £1·30	56p £0·56	85p £0·85	40p £0·40
N	7p £0·07	17p £0·17	9p £0·09	108p £1·08	60p £0·60	110p £1·10

Complete

O	34p−18p=16p	27p−22p=5p	43p−35p=8p	50p−27p=23p
P	61p−37p=24p	80p−17p=63p	55p−28p=27p	83p−48p=35p
Q	94p−66p=28p	52p−26p=26p	76p−39p=37p	62p−19p=43p
R	£1−92p=8p	£1−76p=24p	£1−38p=62p	£1−24p=76p
S	£1−73p=27p	£1−44p=56p	£1−52p=48p	£1−61p=39p
T	£1−85p=15p	£1−29p=71p	£1−43p=57p	£1−37p=63p

Write answers only

A What change should I receive from two tens when paying for a box of chocolates which cost 15p? 5p

B How much should be paid for 7 threepenny stamps? 21p

C What is the total cost of a writing pad at 8p, envelopes at 6p, and a bottle of ink at 7p? 21p

D What is the total cost of five handkerchiefs at 14p each? 70p

E Is 8p the correct change when paying for a gramophone record at 42p with a fifty? Yes

F If 8 pencils cost 24p what is the price of one pencil? 3p

G What sum of money is one quarter of three pounds? 75p

H What is the difference in cost between two chairs if one costs £7·34 and the other £8·10? £0·76 (76p)

I What sum of money is equal to ten fifties? £5

J How much must be added to seven tens to make 2 pounds? £1·30 (130p)

K What should be paid for one peach if a box of nine costs 54p? 6p

L If Tom has saved 37p how much will he have when his father gives him two tens and a five? 62p

M What should each of eight boys receive if they share one pound amongst them? $12\frac{1}{2}$p

N How much had Peter if he had one fifty, four tens and two fives? £1

O After paying 47p for a book Ann had 26p left. How much had she at first? 73p

P Mary had saved 87p to buy presents for Mother and Father. If Father's present cost 39p what was the most that she could pay for Mother's present? 48p

Q What should 3 litres of oil cost if 5 litres costs £1? 60p

R At a Sale towels cost 27p instead of 33p. What did Mother save by buying four towels at Sale price? 24p

See notes on page 80.

MORNING and AFTERNOON

A How many hours are there in one day? 24

B How many hours are there marked on a clock face? 12

Write in figures what would be the time on this clock

C in the morning. 2.25 a.m.

D in the afternoon. 2.25 p.m.

Write in figures

E twenty minutes past three o'clock in the afternoon. 3.20 p.m.

F twenty minutes past three o'clock in the morning. 3.20 a.m.

G half-past seven o'clock in the morning. 7.30 a.m.

H half-past eleven o'clock in the evening. 11.30 p.m.

I twenty-eight minutes past one o'clock in the afternoon. 1.28 p.m.

J twenty-six minutes past twelve o'clock mid-day. 12.26 p.m.

K twenty-minutes to twelve o'clock mid-day. 11.40 a.m.

L five minutes past eight o'clock in the morning. 8.05 a.m.

M seven minutes past three o'clock in the afternoon. 3.07 p.m.

N nine minutes past twelve o'clock mid-day. 12.09 p.m.

O half-past twelve o'clock midnight. 12.30 a.m.

P two minutes past twelve o'clock midnight. 12.02 a.m.

Q a quarter hour before noon. 11.45 a.m.

R a quarter hour after midnight. 12.15 a.m.

S three-quarters of an hour before midnight. 11.15 p.m.

T forty-five minutes after noon. 12.45 p.m.

U a quarter to seven o'clock in the morning. 6.45 a.m.

V fifty minutes after eleven o'clock in the morning. 11.50 a.m.

W fifteen minutes to twelve o'clock midnight. 11.45 p.m.

The teacher should ensure that pupils know the relationships of a.m., p.m., noon and midnight.

Write what would be the correct time if this clock is

A 1 hour fast 7.40
B 20 minutes fast 8.20
C $\frac{1}{4}$ hour slow 8.55
D 25 minutes slow 9.05
E $\frac{3}{4}$ hour fast 7.55

Give the time one hour after

F	4 p.m. 5 p.m.	11.30 a.m. 12.30 p.m.	12 noon 1 p.m.
G	6.05 a.m. 7.05 a.m.	1.45 p.m. 2.45 p.m.	12 midnight 1 a.m.
H	11 a.m. 12 noon	11.30 p.m. 12.30 a.m.	11.50 p.m. 12.50 a.m.

Give the time one hour before

I	2.15 p.m. 1.15 p.m.	5.30 a.m. 4.30 a.m.	12 noon 11 a.m.
J	12.30 p.m. 11.30 a.m.	1.45 p.m. 12.45 p.m.	12 midnight 11 p.m.
K	1.30 a.m. 12.30 a.m.	12.15 a.m. 11.15 p.m.	11.45 p.m. 10.45 p.m.

Give the time two hours before

L	10.18 p.m. 8.18 p.m.	1 p.m. 11 a.m.	2 a.m. 12 midnight
M	2 p.m. 12 noon	1.45 a.m. 11.45 p.m.	11.55 p.m. 9.55 p.m.

Add one half-hour to

N	3.10 a.m. 3.40 a.m.	11.30 a.m. 12 noon	11.45 a.m. 12.15 p.m.
O	12.18 p.m. 12.48 p.m.	11.52 p.m. 12.22 a.m.	12.48 a.m. 1.18 a.m.

P 11.55 a.m. Tues. 12.25 p.m. Tues. 11.55 p.m. Thurs. 12.25 a.m. Friday

---

Give the time one half-hour before

Q	1 a.m. 12.30 a.m.	3.15 a.m. 2.45 a.m.	11.45 p.m. 11.15 p.m.
R	12.15 p.m. 11.45 a.m.	12.25 p.m. 11.55 a.m.	noon 11.30 a.m.
S	12.05 a.m. 11.35 p.m.	10.13 p.m. 9.43 p.m.	midnight 11.30 p.m.

Give the time 12 hours before

T	2.15 p.m. 2.15 a.m.	10.35 p.m. 10.35 a.m.	11.55 p.m. 11.55 a.m.

U 7.30 p.m. Mon. 7.30 a.m. Mon. 12.30 p.m. Wed. 12.30 a.m. Wed.
V 8.45 a.m. Fri. 8.45 p.m. Thur. 4.05 a.m. Sat. 4.05 p.m. Friday

RIGHT ANGLES

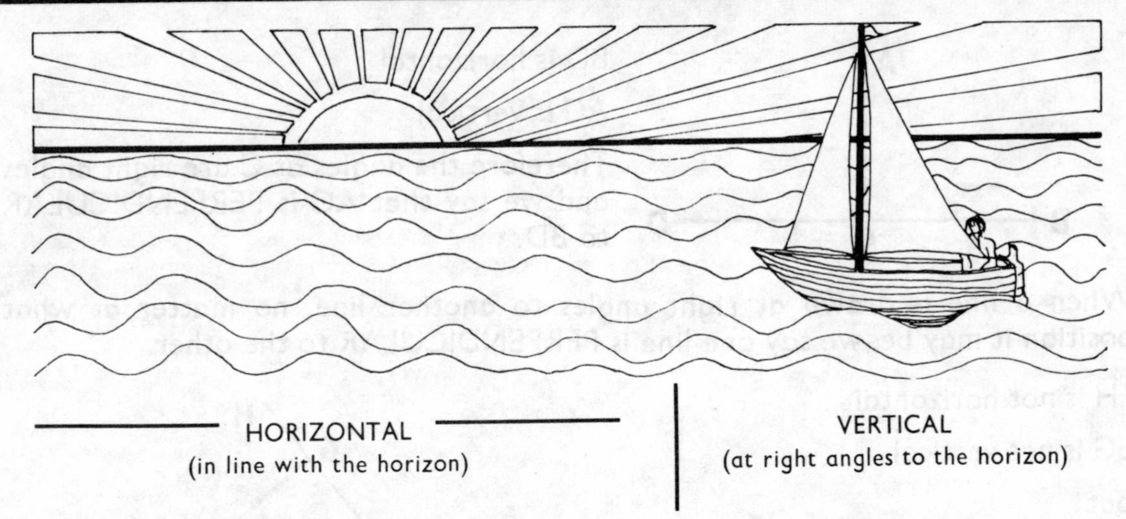

HORIZONTAL
(in line with the horizon)

VERTICAL
(at right angles to the horizon)

Use your dictionary to find the meaning of, "Out of plumb".

Which of these is a RIGHT ANGLE? B, C, E, F

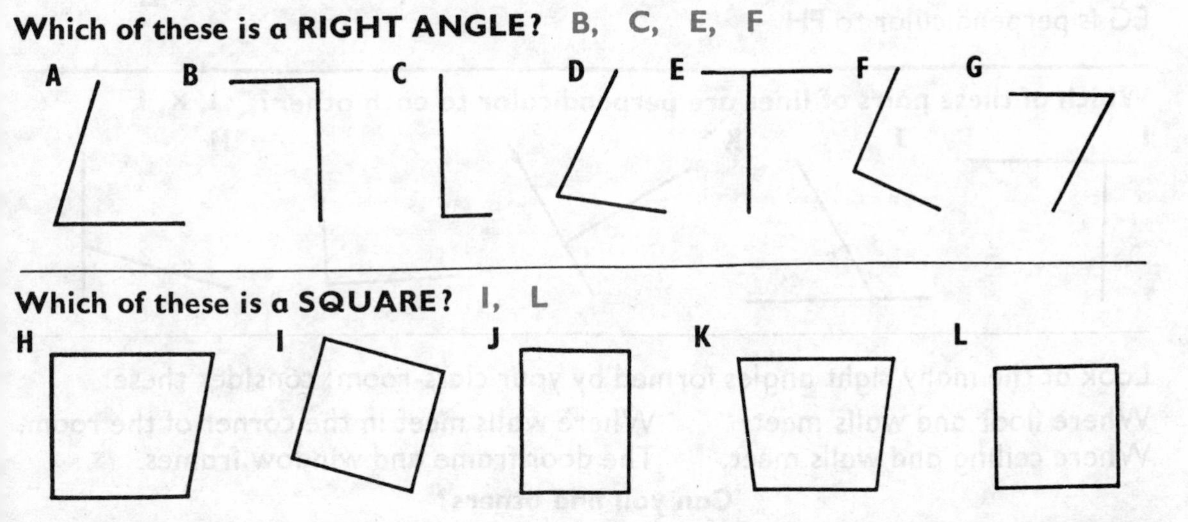

Which of these is a SQUARE? I, L

Only a four-sided figure can enclose four right angles with straight lines. Any such four-sided figure having all its angles right angles is called a rectangle.

Which of these figures are RECTANGLES? M, O, P

M N O P Q

If the properties of a RIGHT ANGLE have not been dealt with in practical work it would be of help to the pupil to make one by folding a circle, and using it to check the answers on this page. Otherwise a set square should be available.

RIGHT ANGLES and TRIANGLES

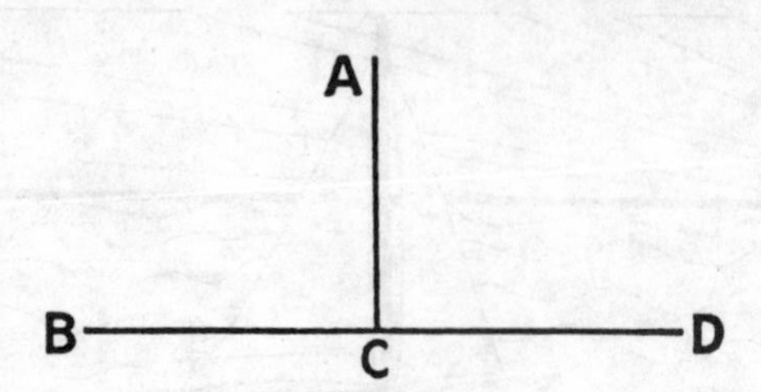

BD is horizontal

AC is vertical

Therefore the angles at C are right angles and we say that AC is PERPENDICULAR to BD.

When a line is drawn at right angles to another line, no matter at what position it may be, we say one line is PERPENDICULAR to the other.

FH is not horizontal

EG is not vertical

but

EG is at right angles to FH and therefore

EG is perpendicular to FH

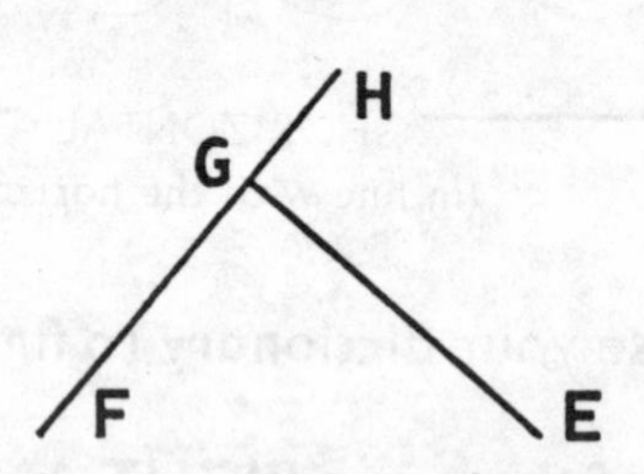

Which of these pairs of lines are perpendicular to each other? I, K, L

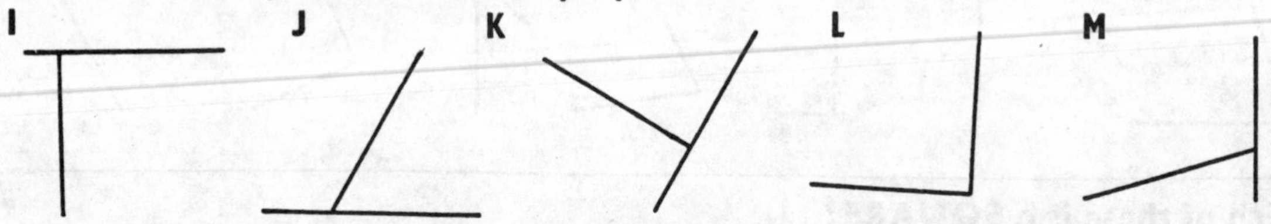

Look at the many right angles formed by your class-room: consider these:

Where floor and walls meet,

Where ceiling and walls meet,

Where walls meet in the corner of the room,

The door frame and window frames.

Can you find others?

Any figure having three straight sides is called a TRIANGLE.

Which of these triangles has no right angle? N, P, R

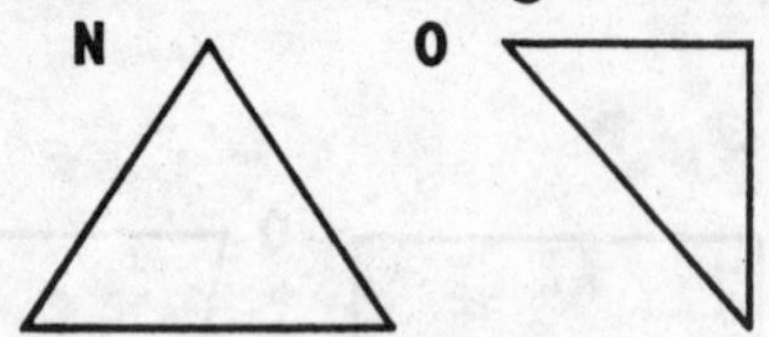

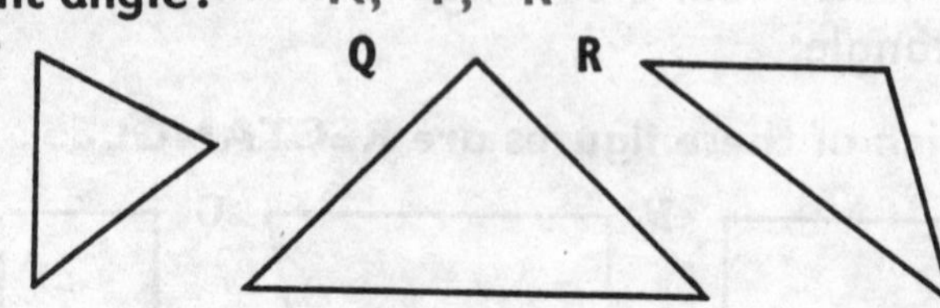

Multiply (×)

A	4× 6=24	5× 5= 25	6× 6=36	8× 3=24	3× 8=24
B	6× 7=42	3× 9= 27	4× 7=28	5× 8=40	7× 3=21
C	7× 4=28	5× 7= 35	6× 5=30	7× 6=42	8× 4=32
D	9× 3=27	10× 2= 20	6× 9=54	7× 5=35	11× 3=33
E	10× 3=30	9× 4= 36	12× 2=24	3×12=36	5×12=60
F	4×11=44	6×10= 60	7×12=84	10× 4=40	6× 8=48
G	8× 7=56	9× 6= 54	12× 8=96	7×10=70	8× 9=72
H	11× 4=44	12× 9=108	7× 7=49	12× 4=48	12× 7=84

Complete these sums

I	5× 6= 30	6× 4= 24	7× 8=56	6×10= 60
J	10× 5= 50	8× 5= 40	8× 6=48	7× 9= 63
K	8× 8= 64	7×10= 70	8× 9=72	9× 5= 45
L	9× 7= 63	9× 8= 72	8×10=80	9× 9= 81
M	9×10= 90	10× 6=60	11× 5=55	11× 6= 66
N	10× 7= 70	11×7= 77	12× 5=60	12× 6= 72
O	7×12= 84	10× 9= 90	11× 8=88	8×12= 96
P	12× 9=108	12×12=144	10× 9=90	12×10=120

Divide (÷)

Q	20÷ 5= 4	24÷ 4= 6	30÷ 6= 5	21÷ 7= 3	24÷ 8= 3
R	27÷ 9= 3	32÷ 8= 4	33÷11= 3	36÷ 9= 4	42÷ 6= 7
S	42÷ 7= 6	45÷ 5= 9	49÷ 7= 7	48÷12= 4	60÷ 5=12
T	54÷ 6= 9	56÷ 7= 8	63÷ 9= 7	64÷ 8= 8	70÷10= 7
U	48÷ 8= 6	35÷ 7= 5	54÷ 9= 6	72÷ 6=12	72÷ 9= 8
V	72÷12= 6	84÷12= 7	77÷ 7=11	81÷ 9= 9	84÷ 7=12
W	72÷ 8= 9	88÷11= 8	100÷10=10	96÷12= 8	108÷12= 9
X	96÷ 8=12	120÷10=12	132÷11=12	108÷ 9=12	144÷12= 12

Multiplication and Division Tables are extended to 12 × 12. Pupils of average ability should be able to achieve 38 correct answers in 4 minutes in group **A–H** and in 5 minutes in groups **I–P** and **Q–X**.

Complete

A	(8×3)+ 4= 28	(7× 6)+ 5= 47	(9× 4)+ 3= 39	(6× 5)+ 4= 34
B	(9×0)+ 2= 2	(8× 0)+ 3= 3	(5× 8)+ 6= 46	(8× 7)+ 5= 61
C	(6×9)+ 3= 57	(5×10)+ 6= 56	(4×12)+ 5= 53	(12× 6)+ 9= 81
D	(7×0)+ 8= 8	(12× 0)+10= 10	(8× 8)+ 7= 71	(9× 9)+ 8= 89
E	(9×8)+ 7= 79	(12× 7)+ 8= 92	(8×11)+ 9= 97	(12× 8)+10= 106
F	(12×9)+11= 119	(10×12)+ 0= 120	(11×11)+10= 131	(12×12)+11= 155

Multiply (×)

G	908 × 5 = 4540	709 × 6 = 4254	750 × 7 = 5250	630 × 8 = 5040	820 × 8 = 6560	432 × 9 = 3888
H	523 × 11 = 5753	989 × 10 = 9890	367 × 12 = 4404	725 × 12 = 8700	825 × 12 = 9900	467 × 11 = 5137
I	999 × 11 = 10989	875 × 12 = 10500	884 × 12 = 10608	909 × 10 = 9090	798 × 11 = 8778	899 × 12 = 10788

Work out these sums

J What number is equal to the product of six and seven-hundred-and-ninety? 4 740

K How many pints of milk are equal to 637 gallons? 5 096

L If each of nine crates holds one-hundred-and-fifty oranges what is the total number of oranges? 1 350 oranges

M What is the total quantity of bricks delivered by eight lorries if each carries 675 bricks? 5 400 bricks

N If there are twelve rows of seats in an open-air theatre, each row having one-hundred-and-nine seats, what is the total number of people that can be seated? 1 308 people

O Is the product of eight-hundred-and-seventy and nine, greater or less than the product of nine-hundred-and-seventy and eight? greater

See notes on page 80.

SPEED PRACTICE

Divide (÷)

A	18÷ 6= 3	27÷ 9= 3	21÷ 4=5r1	27÷ 6=4r3	27÷ 5= 5r2
B	26÷ 7= 3r5	26÷ 8= 3r2	30÷ 9=3r3	30÷12=2r6	30÷11= 2r8
C	37÷ 8= 4r5	41÷ 7= 5r6	52÷ 6=8r4	51÷ 9=5r6	57÷12= 4r9
D	62÷ 5=12r2	70÷11= 6r4	66÷ 7=9r3	69÷ 8=8r5	71÷ 9= 7r8
E	75÷ 8= 9r3	80÷ 7=11r3	85÷ 9=9r4	79÷10=7r9	83÷11= 7r6
F	84÷12= 7	91÷11= 8r3	93÷10=9r3	87÷ 9=9r6	94÷ 8=11r6
G	102÷ 9=11r3	103÷ 8=12r7	111÷12=9r3	108÷11=9r9	117÷12= 9r9

Divide (÷)

H	900r1 9)8101	901r2 8)7210	905r8 9)8153	1011r2 8)8090	910 9)8190
I	889r4 9)8005	100 10)1000	100 11)1100	950r3 10)9503	418r2 11)4600
J	428 11)4708	806r1 10)8061	254r2 12)3050	277r9 12)3333	546 11)6006
K	970 10)9700	364r1 12)4369	375 12)4500	362r8 11)3990	450r1 12)5401

Write answers only

L Into how many groups of three can you arrange 24 cakes? 8

M How many times can eight be taken from forty-eight? 6

N How many elevens are equal to seventy-seven? 7

O Find how many children can have four cakes each from a tray containing forty-eight cakes. 12 children

P Will nine divide exactly into eighty-three? No

Q What number is one-eighth of forty-eight? 6

R How many boxes will be needed to pack one-hundred-and-eight peaches if each box holds twelve peaches? 9

SPEED PRACTICE

Divide (÷)

A	32 ÷ 7 = 4r4	41 ÷ 12 = 3r5	35 ÷ 9 = 3r8	50 ÷ 11 = 4r6	43 ÷ 10 = 4r3
B	62 ÷ 8 = 7r6	66 ÷ 10 = 6r6	71 ÷ 8 = 8r7	82 ÷ 12 = 6r10	61 ÷ 9 = 6r7
C	63 ÷ 11 = 5r8	93 ÷ 12 = 7r9	90 ÷ 11 = 8r2	88 ÷ 10 = 8r8	77 ÷ 8 = 9r5
D	84 ÷ 9 = 9r3	95 ÷ 10 = 9r5	106 ÷ 12 = 8r10	119 ÷ 12 = 9r11	109 ÷ 11 = 9r1

Divide (÷)

E	6)504 = 84	8)900 = 112r4	7)766 = 109r3	9)815 = 90r5	11)560 = 50r10
F	11)3311 = 301	9)2705 = 300r5	7)6400 = 914r2	8)9043 = 1130r3	12)4810 = 400r10
G	10)5233 = 523r3	9)7240 = 804r4	11)1001 = 91	10)1818 = 181r8	12)1068 = 89
H	12)2208 = 184	12)5820 = 485	11)9909 = 900r9	12)7000 = 583r4	10)1357 = 135r7

Work out these sums

I What number is one-sixth of three-thousand-and-sixty? 510

J 392 children are to travel in 7 coaches. How many children will there be in each coach? 56 children

K How many nines are there in one-thousand-and-eighty? 120

L A car takes 8 hours to travel 296 kilometres. How many kilometres is that for each hour of travelling? 37 kilometres

M A poultry farmer agrees to supply a large hotel with three-thousand dressed chickens during one year. How many is that for each month? 250 chickens

N Which number should we have to multiply by eleven to make one-thousand-and-seventy-eight? 98

Write these shortened words in full

A Fri. Friday Sat. Saturday Tue. Tuesday Wed. Wednesday
Mon. Monday Sun. Sunday Thu. Thursday

Write in full each day of the week in the correct order beginning with

B Sunday, Monday, Tuesday, Wednesday, Thursday, Friday, Saturday

Write how many days there are in

C one week 7 two weeks 14 three weeks 21

Name the day which comes before

D Wednesday Tuesday Saturday Friday Monday Sunday

Name the day which comes two days after

E Sunday Tuesday Tuesday Thursday Friday Sunday

Learn the order and how to spell the names of the months

January, February, March, April, May, June, July, August, September, October, November, December.

Name the month which comes after

F January February August September November December
April May September October March April

Name the month which comes before

G July June November Oct. March Feb. June May
December Nov. October Sept. May April January Dec.

Name which month comes before and which comes after

H February Jan.–Mar. May Apr.–June October Sept.–Nov.

Name which month is two months after

I January March July Sept. November Jan.

Look at this month's page of the Calendar

J How many days are in this month?
K Name the first day of the month.
L Name the last day of the month.
M On which day is the 3rd? the 15th? the 26th?
N What is the date of the second Tuesday of the month?
O What is the date of the last Friday of the month?

THE CALENDAR

Learn these facts and this poem

In one Year there are
365 days
52 weeks
12 Calendar months
but in a Leap Year
there are 366 days.

Thirty days hath September,
April, June and November.
All the rest have thirty-one,
Excepting February alone,
Which has twenty-eight days clear,
But twenty-nine each Leap Year.

Which of these were Leap Years?

A 1932 Yes 1940 Yes 1946 No 1950 No 1952 Yes 1962 No

Which of these will be Leap Years?

B 1970 No 1975 No 1980 Yes 1988 Yes 1990 No 1992 Yes

Which Leap Year

C was the last? will be the next?

How many days will there be in each of these months?

D January 31 April 30 June 30
E August 31 November 30 December 31
F February 1974 28 February 1976 29 February 1978 28

If 1st June was on Wednesday give the date of these days in the same week

G Friday 3rd June Tuesday 31st May Sunday 29th May

If 1st July was on Thursday give the date of these days in the same week

H Saturday 3rd July Tuesday 29th June Sunday 27th June

Write how many days there are from

I 2nd Aug. to 10th Aug. 8 20th May to 30th May 10
J 25th Apr. to 2nd May 7 30th June to 15th July 15
K 20th Feb. '74 to 2nd Mar. '74 10 20th Dec. '72 to 10th Jan. '73 21

January is month No. 1. Put the number against each of these

L March 3 July 7 September 9 April 4 October 10 June 6

If "7.8.72" stands for "7 August 1972" write what is short for

M 3rd Feb. 1970 3.2.70 16th Aug. 1974 16.8.74 30th Dec. 1972 30.12.72
N 9th June 1971 9.6.71 31st Jan. 1975 31.1.75 23rd Mar. 1977 23.3.77
O 2nd May 1970 2.5.70 30th Nov. 1978 30.11.78 1st Sept. 1971 1.9.71

It would be appropriate at this stage for the pupils to write in figures the dates of the last birthday, the next birthday and the date of birth, and their present ages in years and completed months.

GENERAL REVISION

A	3+ 5= 8	16+7=23	9−6= 3	12− 7= 5	23+ 9=32
B	7× 3=21	4×8=32	15÷5= 3	18÷ 9= 2	24÷ 3= 8
C	18− 9= 9	32÷8= 4	7×9=63	12× 8=96	54÷ 9= 6
D	9× 8=72	12×6=72	64÷8= 8	96÷12= 8	9×12=108
E	17÷ 4=4r1	33÷6=5r3	50÷7=7r1	56÷ 6=9r2	60÷ 8=7r4
F	80÷11=7r3	60÷7=8r4	85÷9=9r4	102÷11=9r3	112÷12=9r4

G $2\frac{1}{2}$ hours= 5 half-hours $1\frac{3}{4}$ hours= 7 quarter-hours

H Write the time that is one hour before noon. 11 a.m.

I Write the time that is one half-hour after noon. 12.30 p.m.

State in figures

J 5th June 1971 5.6.71 20th Mar. 1970 20.3.70 2nd Sept. 1972 2.9.72

State how many days there are from

K 23rd Feb. '72 to 3rd Mar. '72 9 25th Dec. '72 to 17th Jan. '72 23

Complete

L	32p+20p=52p	48p+34p=82p	67p+26p=93p	38p+49p=87p
M	68p+40p=£1·08	57p+48p=£1·05	78p+58p=£1·36	69p+86p=£1·55
N	30p−23p= 7p	50p−16p=34p	83p−58p=25p	£1−64p=36p
O	70p−62p= 8p	81p−45p=36p	50p−27p=23p	£1−36p=64p

Add (+)

P

$$\begin{array}{r} 375 \\ 408 \\ 96 \\ 821 \\ \hline 1700 \end{array} \qquad \begin{array}{r} 4268 \\ 907 \\ 85 \\ 8769 \\ \hline 14029 \end{array}$$

Subtract (−)

$$\begin{array}{r} 703 \\ -\ 85 \\ \hline 618 \end{array} \qquad \begin{array}{r} 5701 \\ -\ 964 \\ \hline 4737 \end{array} \qquad \begin{array}{r} 8005 \\ -\ 7906 \\ \hline 99 \end{array}$$

Multiply (×)

Q

$$\begin{array}{r} 496 \\ \times\ 9 \\ \hline 4464 \end{array} \qquad \begin{array}{r} 789 \\ \times\ 12 \\ \hline 9468 \end{array}$$

Divide (÷)

$$7\overline{)900} = 128r4 \qquad 9\overline{)5092} = 565r7 \qquad 11\overline{)1003} = 91r2$$

SQUARES, RECTANGLES and TRIANGLES

A Can you find 5 squares and 4 oblongs in this figure?

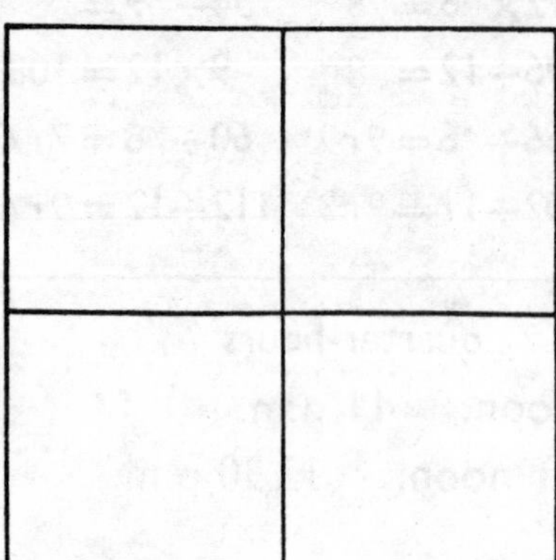

B Can you find 8 squares and 10 oblongs in this figure?

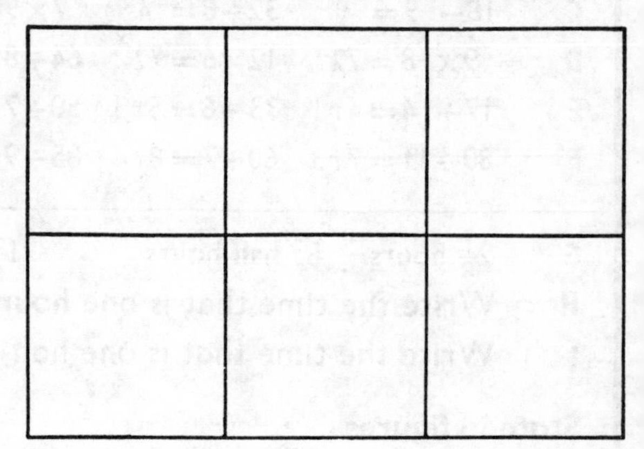

C Can you find 4 triangles in this figure?

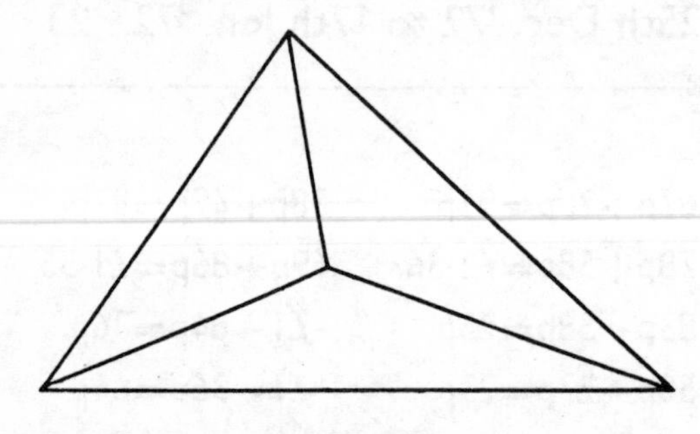

D Can you find 4 triangles in this figure?

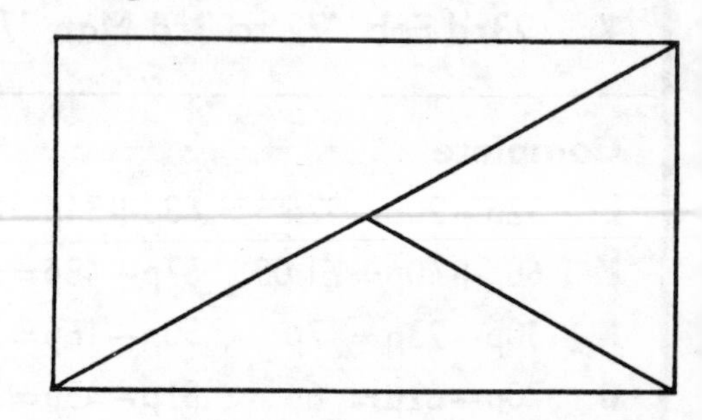

E Can you find 14 squares and 22 oblongs in this figure?

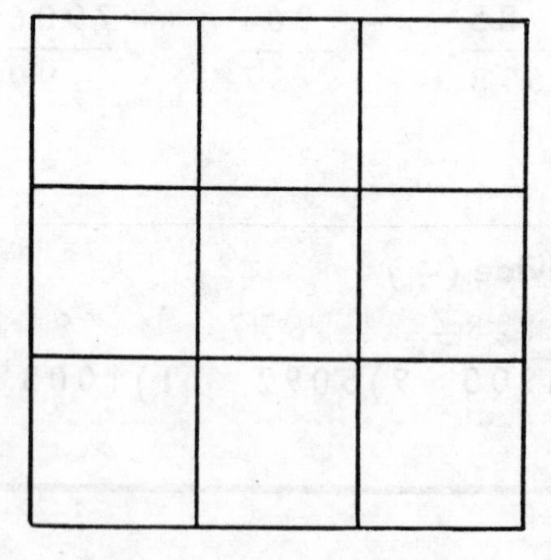

F Can you find 8 triangles in this figure?

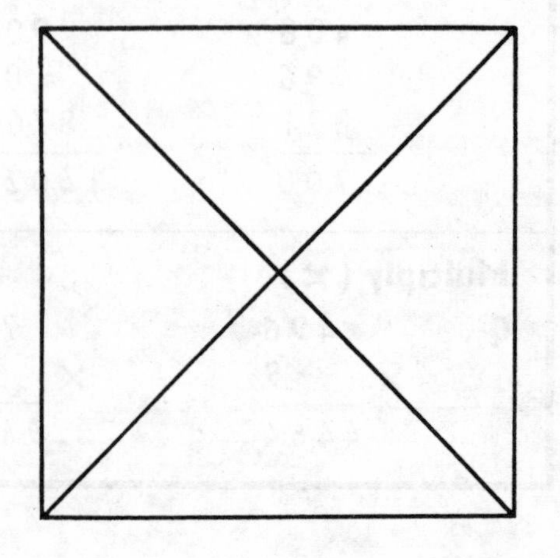

Some pupils may obtain assistance by using a Shapes Board.

Here is a rectangle divided into four equal sections.

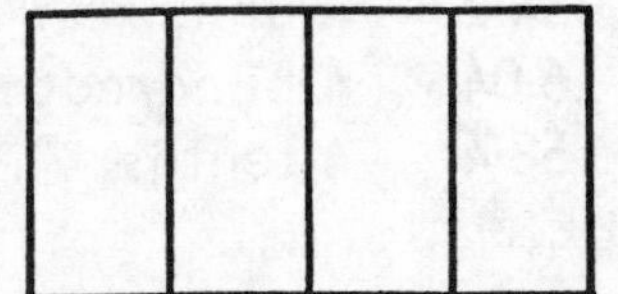

A How wide is each section? 9 mm

B You draw a rectangle 48 mm by 20 mm and divide it similarly into four sections.

Say what length a rectangle would be if it were similarly divided into

C 3 sections of $\frac{1}{2}$cm $1\frac{1}{2}$cm 5 sections of 7 mm 35 mm 4 sections of $2\frac{1}{2}$cm 10 cm

---

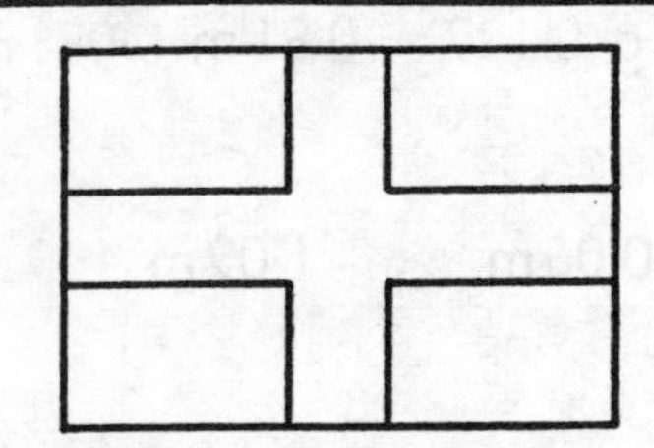

Here is the flag of St. George.

D You draw a similar flag, making all of your measurements twice the size of those in this drawing.

E Measure the length and width of the flag in the drawing above, and then work out the total distance round all the four sides. 12 cm 6 mm

The distance around any shape we call the PERIMETER.

Find the perimeter of each of these Rectangles and Triangles

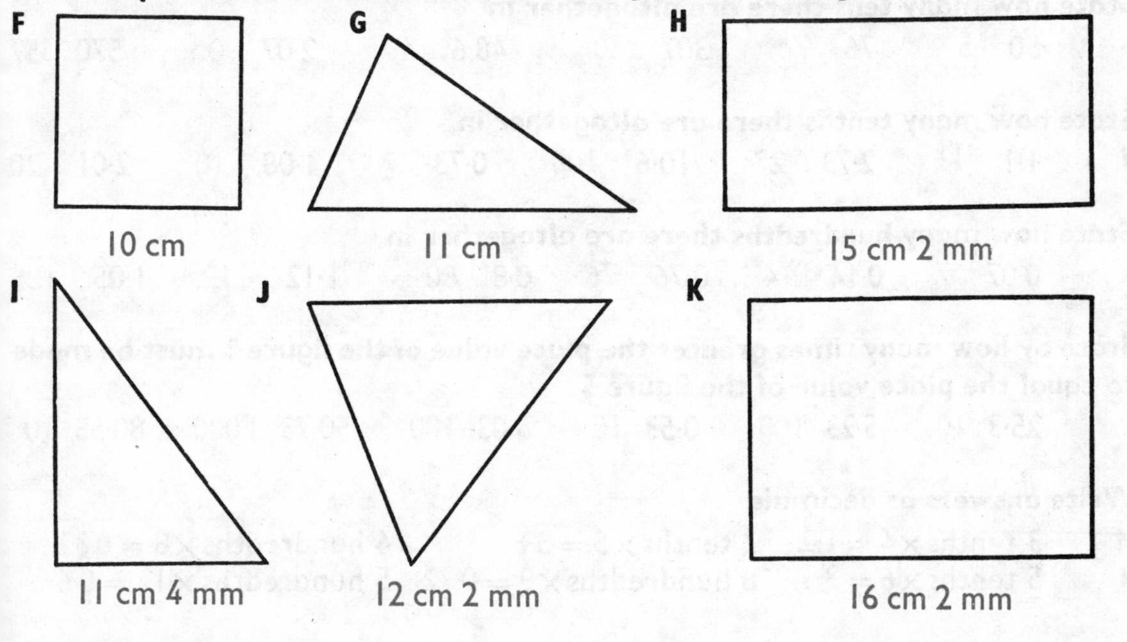

State the place value of the figure 4 in each number

A	342	4 tens	3·42	4 tenths	34·2	4 units
B	406	4 hundreds	40·6	4 tens	6·04	4 hundredths
C	584	4 units	5·84	4 hundredths	58·4	4 tenths

Multiply each number by 10

D 8p 80p 7 m 70 m 0·7 m 7 m 35p £3·50 2·06 l 20·6 l 50 g 500 g

Divide each number by 10

E 70p 7p £3 £0·30 £0·20 £0·02 0·6 m 0·06 m 1·37 g 0·137 g 0·81 m 0·081 m

Multiply each number by 100

F 2 m 200 m 0·2 m 20 m 0·02 l 2 l £0·17 £17 0·06 m 6 m 1·09 m 109 m

Divide each number by 100

G £40 £0·40 5 m 0·05 m 50p ½p £300 £3 £270 £2·70 7 l 0·07 l

State how many units there are altogether in

H 5 5 25 25 3·4 3 2·06 2 0·26 0 370 370

State how many tens there are altogether in

I 50 5 76 7 307 30 48·6 4 2·07 0 570 57

State how many tenths there are altogether in

J 1·1 11 2·73 27 10·6 106 0·73 7 1·08 10 2·01 20

State how many hundredths there are altogether in

K 0·07 7 0·14 14 0·76 76 0·8 80 1·12 112 1·05 105

State by how many times greater the place value of the figure 3 must be made to equal the place value of the figure 5

L 25·3 10 5·23 100 0·53 10 5·03 100 50·73 1 000 80·53 10

Write answers as decimals

M	3 tenths × 4 = 1·2	7 tenths × 5 = 3·5	4 hundredths × 8 = 0·32
N	5 tenths × 6 = 3	8 hundredths × 9 = 0·72	5 hundredths × 12 = 0·6

Multiply: under each answer rewrite it in its true pound form

A	73p	65p	86p	73p	78p	85p
	× 6	× 8	× 7	× 11	× 9	× 12
	438p	520p	602p	803p	702p	1020p
	£4·38	£5·20	£6·02	£8·03	£7·02	£10·20

Write answers only

B	$\frac{1}{2}$p×2= 1p	$\frac{1}{2}$p×3= $1\frac{1}{2}$p	$\frac{1}{2}$p× 5= $2\frac{1}{2}$p	$\frac{1}{2}$p× 4= 2p
C	$\frac{1}{2}$p×6= 3p	$\frac{1}{2}$p×7= $3\frac{1}{2}$p	$\frac{1}{2}$p×11= $5\frac{1}{2}$p	$\frac{1}{2}$p×12= 6p
D	$1\frac{1}{2}$p×2= 3p	$1\frac{1}{2}$p×3= $4\frac{1}{2}$p	$2\frac{1}{2}$p× 2= 5p	$2\frac{1}{2}$p× 3= $7\frac{1}{2}$p
E	$1\frac{1}{2}$p×5= $7\frac{1}{2}$p	$1\frac{1}{2}$p×8= 12p	$1\frac{1}{2}$p× 6= 9p	$2\frac{1}{2}$p× 7= $17\frac{1}{2}$p
F	$3\frac{1}{2}$p×4= 14p	$2\frac{1}{2}$p×9= $22\frac{1}{2}$p	$5\frac{1}{2}$p× 9= $49\frac{1}{2}$p	$7\frac{1}{2}$p×10= 75p

Under each answer rewrite it in its true pound form

G	$13\frac{1}{2}$p	$21\frac{1}{2}$p	$16\frac{1}{2}$p	$18\frac{1}{2}$p	$27\frac{1}{2}$p	$34\frac{1}{2}$p
	× 5	× 6	× 5	× 8	× 5	× 9
	$67\frac{1}{2}$p	129p	$82\frac{1}{2}$p	148p	$137\frac{1}{2}$p	$310\frac{1}{2}$p
	£0·$67\frac{1}{2}$	£1·29	£0·$82\frac{1}{2}$	£1·48	£1·$37\frac{1}{2}$	£3·$10\frac{1}{2}$
H	$26\frac{1}{2}$p	$45\frac{1}{2}$p	$19\frac{1}{2}$p	$37\frac{1}{2}$p	$27\frac{1}{2}$p	$18\frac{1}{2}$p
	× 7	× 9	× 10	× 9	× 8	× 12
	$185\frac{1}{2}$p	$409\frac{1}{2}$p	195p	$337\frac{1}{2}$p	220p	222p
	£1·$85\frac{1}{2}$	£4·$09\frac{1}{2}$	£1·95	£3·$37\frac{1}{2}$	£2·20	£2·22
I	$18\frac{1}{2}$p	$24\frac{1}{2}$p	$37\frac{1}{2}$p	$20\frac{1}{2}$p	$33\frac{1}{2}$p	$27\frac{1}{2}$p
	× 6	× 9	× 8	× 11	× 9	× 12
	111p	$220\frac{1}{2}$p	300p	$225\frac{1}{2}$p	$301\frac{1}{2}$p	330p
	£1·11	£2·$20\frac{1}{2}$	£3	£2·$25\frac{1}{2}$	£3·$01\frac{1}{2}$	£3·30
J	$40\frac{1}{2}$p	$39\frac{1}{2}$p	$78\frac{1}{2}$p	$87\frac{1}{2}$p	$58\frac{1}{2}$p	$45\frac{1}{2}$p
	× 10	× 7	× 9	× 8	× 12	× 11
	405p	$276\frac{1}{2}$p	$706\frac{1}{2}$p	700p	702p	$500\frac{1}{2}$p
	£4·05	£2·$76\frac{1}{2}$	£7·$06\frac{1}{2}$	£7	£7·02	£5·$00\frac{1}{2}$

MULTIPLICATION OF POUNDS AND PENCE

Write answers only. Work across the page

A	0·3 ×4= 1·2	0·2 ×6= 1·2	0·5 ×5= 2·5	0·7 ×8= 5·6
B	0·2 ×5= 1	0·5 ×8= 4	0·7 ×9= 6·3	0·8 ×5= 4
C	0·03×2= 0·06	0·04×2= 0·08	0·04×3= 0·12	0·06×4= 0·24
D	0·06×9= 0·54	0·07×6= 0·42	0·08×7= 0·56	0·09×9= 0·81

Multiply (×)

E	£1·32 × 4 = £5·28	£2·15 × 7 = £15·05	£1·63 × 6 = £9·78	£2·72 × 8 = £21·76	£3·16 × 9 = £28·44
F	£2·06 × 7 = £14·42	£3·09 × 8 = £24·72	£4·05 × 11 = £44·55	£1·75 × 8 = £14·00	£3·05 × 12 = £36·60
G	£5·60 × 5 = £28	£3·50 × 8 = £28	£6·09 × 9 = £54·81	£5·09 × 12 = £61·08	£4·78 × 9 = £43·02
H	£1·31½ × 5 = £6·57½	£1·24½ × 6 = £7·47	£2·65½ × 7 = £18·58½	£1·86½ × 6 = £11·19	£1·37½ × 9 = £12·37½
I	£0·64½ × 10 = £6·45	£0·38½ × 8 = £3·08	£0·87½ × 9 = £7·87½	£1·96½ × 11 = £21·61½	£2·89½ × 12 = £34·74
J	£0·78½ × 9 = £7·06½	£6·08 × 7 = £42·56	£7·09 × 9 = £63·81	£5·80 × 12 = £69·60	£6·50 × 8 = £52
K	£1·08½ × 8 = £8·68	£2·70½ × 9 = £24·34½	£1·90½ × 11 = £20·95½	£6·98 × 12 = £83·76	£1·09½ × 12 = £13·14

See notes on page 81.

A	1 unit = 10 tenths	3 units = 30 tenths
B	1 tenth = 10 hundredths	2 tenths = 20 hundredths
C	4 tenths = 40 hundredths	7 tenths = 70 hundredths
D	1·1 = 11 tenths	1·3 = 13 tenths
E	2·4 = 24 tenths	3·7 = 37 tenths
F	0·12 = 12 hundredths	0·18 = 18 hundredths
G	0·26 = 26 hundredths	0·43 = 43 hundredths

H How many tens are there in £1? 10 £2? 20 £5? 50 £8? 80

I How many pence are there in 1 ten? 10 3 tens? 30 6 tens? 60

Divide (÷)

J	£1·26	£1·42	£1·23	£1·53	£1·32
	2)£2·52	3)£4·26	5)£6·15	4)£6·12	7)£9·24
K	£1·06	£1·06	£1·33	£1·44	£1·23
	4)£4·24	6)£6·36	8)£10·64	7)£10·08	9)£11·07
L	£1·21	£1·22	£1·21	£1·35	£1·26
	7)£8·47	8)£9·76	11)£13·31	10)£13·50	12)£15·12
M	£2·08	£3·06	£2·50	£1·90	£1·40
	6)£12·48	9)£27·54	7)£17·50	12)£22·80	11)£15·40
N	£0·22	£0·37	£0·23	£0·44	£0·35
	8)£1·76	7)£2·59	11)£2·53	9)£3·96	12)£4·20
O	£0·43	£0·37	£0·34	£0·55	£0·84
	7)£3·01	11)£4·07	9)£3·06	11)£6·05	12)£10·08
P	£0·09	£0·12	£0·08	£0·09	£0·09
	6)£0·54	8)£0·96	11)£0·88	12)£1·08	9)£0·81

DIVISION OF MONEY

In these sums remember we have two figures only after the point so you will have some remainders. Write them as pence

A 6) £7·34 = £1·22r2p 5) £8·26 = £1·65r1p 7) £9·05 = £1·29r2p 9) £10·11 = £1·12r3p 8) £10·74 = £1·34r2p

B 8) £3·55 = £0·44r3p 7) £3·04 = £0·43r3p 9) £5·00 = £0·55r5p 11) £4·00 = £0·36r4p 12) £10·06 = £0·83r10p

C 5) £3·02 = £0·60r2p 8) £4·06 = £0·50r6p 6) £4·25 = £0·70r5p 9) £9·56 = £1·06r2p 11) £7·00 = £0·63r7p

D 6) £4·40 = £0·73r2p 7) £3 = £0·42r6p 9) £6 = £0·66r6p 11) £8 = £0·72r8p 12) £30 = £2·50

E How many halfpence in $1\frac{1}{2}$p? 3 3p? 6 $2\frac{1}{2}$p? 5 $7\frac{1}{2}$p? 15 $5\frac{1}{2}$p? 11
4p? 8 8p? 16 $6\frac{1}{2}$p? 13 $9\frac{1}{2}$p? 19 11p? 22

F Share 2p amongst 4 children. $\frac{1}{2}$p Share 3p amongst 6 children. $\frac{1}{2}$p

G Share $1\frac{1}{2}$p amongst 3 children. $\frac{1}{2}$p Share $2\frac{1}{2}$p amongst 5 children. $\frac{1}{2}$p

H Share $3\frac{1}{2}$p amongst 7 children. $\frac{1}{2}$p Share 5p amongst 10 children. $\frac{1}{2}$p

I Share 4p amongst 8 children. $\frac{1}{2}$p Share $4\frac{1}{2}$p amongst 9 children. $\frac{1}{2}$p

Do these sums by changing left-over pence into halfpence and dividing again to get the final answer

J 3p ÷ 6 = $\frac{1}{2}$p $4\frac{1}{2}$p ÷ 3 = $1\frac{1}{2}$p $10\frac{1}{2}$p ÷ 3 = $3\frac{1}{2}$p $13\frac{1}{2}$p ÷ 3 = $4\frac{1}{2}$p

K $7\frac{1}{2}$p ÷ 5 = $1\frac{1}{2}$p $12\frac{1}{2}$p ÷ 5 = $2\frac{1}{2}$p 21p ÷ 6 = $3\frac{1}{2}$p $10\frac{1}{2}$p ÷ 7 = $1\frac{1}{2}$p

L 33p ÷ 6 = $5\frac{1}{2}$p 20p ÷ 8 = $2\frac{1}{2}$p $24\frac{1}{2}$p ÷ 7 = $3\frac{1}{2}$p $4\frac{1}{2}$p ÷ 9 = $\frac{1}{2}$p

M 36p ÷ 8 = $4\frac{1}{2}$p $3\frac{1}{2}$p ÷ 7 = $\frac{1}{2}$p 6p ÷ 12 = $\frac{1}{2}$p $38\frac{1}{2}$p ÷ 11 = $3\frac{1}{2}$p

N $38\frac{1}{2}$p ÷ 7 = $5\frac{1}{2}$p 44p ÷ 11 = 4p $31\frac{1}{2}$p ÷ 9 = $3\frac{1}{2}$p 30p ÷ 12 = $2\frac{1}{2}$p

O 35p ÷ 10 = $3\frac{1}{2}$p $40\frac{1}{2}$p ÷ 9 = $4\frac{1}{2}$p 90p ÷ 12 = $7\frac{1}{2}$p $60\frac{1}{2}$p ÷ 11 = $5\frac{1}{2}$p

DIVISION OF MONEY

After changing left-over pence into halfpence and dividing again, state what is finally left over as pence

A	15p ÷ 4 = 3$\frac{1}{2}$p r 1p	13$\frac{1}{2}$p ÷ 5 = 2$\frac{1}{2}$p r 1p	19$\frac{1}{2}$p ÷ 5 = 3$\frac{1}{2}$p r 2p
B	19p ÷ 4 = 4$\frac{1}{2}$p r 1p	24p ÷ 5 = 4$\frac{1}{2}$p r 1$\frac{1}{2}$p	26p ÷ 7 = 3$\frac{1}{2}$p r 1$\frac{1}{2}$p
C	40$\frac{1}{2}$p ÷ 6 = 6$\frac{1}{2}$p r 1$\frac{1}{2}$p	37$\frac{1}{2}$p ÷ 8 = 4$\frac{1}{2}$p r 1$\frac{1}{2}$p	27$\frac{1}{2}$p ÷ 10 = 2$\frac{1}{2}$p r 2$\frac{1}{2}$p
D	34$\frac{1}{2}$p ÷ 5 = 6$\frac{1}{2}$p r 2p	33$\frac{1}{2}$p ÷ 7 = 4$\frac{1}{2}$p r 2p	53$\frac{1}{2}$p ÷ 6 = 8$\frac{1}{2}$p r 2$\frac{1}{2}$p
E	47p ÷ 10 = 4$\frac{1}{2}$p r 2p	53p ÷ 9 = 5$\frac{1}{2}$p r 3$\frac{1}{2}$p	52p ÷ 11 = 4$\frac{1}{2}$p r 2$\frac{1}{2}$p
F	69p ÷ 12 = 5$\frac{1}{2}$p r 3p	86$\frac{1}{2}$p ÷ 10 = 8$\frac{1}{2}$p r 1$\frac{1}{2}$p	81$\frac{1}{2}$p ÷ 12 = 6$\frac{1}{2}$p r 3$\frac{1}{2}$p
G	87$\frac{1}{2}$p ÷ 9 = 9$\frac{1}{2}$p r 2p	93p ÷ 12 = 7$\frac{1}{2}$p r 3p	75$\frac{1}{2}$p ÷ 11 = 6$\frac{1}{2}$p r 4p

H

£2·04$\frac{1}{2}$	£2·01$\frac{1}{2}$	£1·26$\frac{1}{2}$ r$\frac{1}{2}$p	£1·34$\frac{1}{2}$ r1p	£1·41$\frac{1}{2}$
4)£8·18	6)£12·09	5)£6·33	7)£9·42$\frac{1}{2}$	8)£11·32

I

£1·61$\frac{1}{2}$ r$\frac{1}{2}$p	£1·67$\frac{1}{2}$	£1·48 r3$\frac{1}{2}$p	£2·27$\frac{1}{2}$ r2$\frac{1}{2}$p	£2·91 r2p
5)£8·08	6)£10·05	8)£11·87$\frac{1}{2}$	9)£20·50	7)£20·39

J

£1·09$\frac{1}{2}$ r2p	£4·07$\frac{1}{2}$ r1$\frac{1}{2}$p	£2·30$\frac{1}{2}$ r2$\frac{1}{2}$p	£3·80$\frac{1}{2}$ r2p	£2·60$\frac{1}{2}$ r2$\frac{1}{2}$p
7)£7·68$\frac{1}{2}$	5)£20·39	9)£20·77	8)£30·46	11)£28·68

K

£0·45$\frac{1}{2}$ r1p	£0·71 r3p	£0·82$\frac{1}{2}$ r$\frac{1}{2}$p	£0·77$\frac{1}{2}$ r2$\frac{1}{2}$p	£1·58 r4p
8)£3·65	7)£5·00	11)£9·08	9)£7·00	12)£19·00

L

£0·83$\frac{1}{2}$	£0·67$\frac{1}{2}$ r1$\frac{1}{2}$p	£0·98$\frac{1}{2}$ r2p	£0·88 r4p	£0·93$\frac{1}{2}$ r1$\frac{1}{2}$p
6)£5·01	9)£6·09	8)£7·90	12)£10·60	11)£10·30

M

£0·35$\frac{1}{2}$ r2p	£0·45 r$\frac{1}{2}$p	£0·20$\frac{1}{2}$ r3$\frac{1}{2}$p	£0·30$\frac{1}{2}$ r4$\frac{1}{2}$p	£0·50$\frac{1}{2}$ r2p
7)£2·50$\frac{1}{2}$	8)£3·60$\frac{1}{2}$	10)£2·08$\frac{1}{2}$	11)£3·40	12)£6·08

N

£1·44 r4p	£0·07$\frac{1}{2}$ r3$\frac{1}{2}$p	£0·73$\frac{1}{2}$ r2p	£0·12$\frac{1}{2}$ r$\frac{1}{2}$p	£2·10$\frac{1}{2}$ r5p
9)£13	11)£0·86	11)£8·10$\frac{1}{2}$	12)£1·50$\frac{1}{2}$	11)£23·20$\frac{1}{2}$

FRACTIONS

Look carefully at this frame and use it to find some of your answers

<table>
<tr><th colspan="10">A WHOLE ONE</th></tr>
<tr><td colspan="5">$\frac{1}{2}$</td><td colspan="5">$\frac{1}{2}$</td></tr>
<tr><td colspan="2">$\frac{1}{5}$</td><td colspan="2">$\frac{1}{5}$</td><td colspan="2">$\frac{1}{5}$</td><td colspan="2">$\frac{1}{5}$</td><td colspan="2">$\frac{1}{5}$</td></tr>
<tr><td>$\frac{1}{10}$</td><td>$\frac{1}{10}$</td><td>$\frac{1}{10}$</td><td>$\frac{1}{10}$</td><td>$\frac{1}{10}$</td><td>$\frac{1}{10}$</td><td>$\frac{1}{10}$</td><td>$\frac{1}{10}$</td><td>$\frac{1}{10}$</td><td>$\frac{1}{10}$</td></tr>
</table>

A How many fifths equal a whole one? 5

B How many tenths equal a whole one? 10

C Is there an exact number of fifths to equal a half? No

D How many tenths equal one half? 5

E How many tenths equal one fifth? 2

Complete

F	$\frac{1}{2}=\frac{5}{10}$	$\frac{1}{5}=\frac{2}{10}$	$\frac{2}{5}=\frac{4}{10}$	$\frac{4}{5}=\frac{8}{10}$	$\frac{3}{5}=\frac{6}{10}$
G	$\frac{1}{5}+\frac{1}{5}=\frac{2}{5}$	$\frac{2}{5}+\frac{1}{5}=\frac{3}{5}$	$\frac{1}{5}+\frac{2}{5}=\frac{3}{5}$	$\frac{2}{5}+\frac{2}{5}=\frac{4}{5}$	$\frac{3}{5}+\frac{1}{5}=\frac{4}{5}$
H	$1=\frac{2}{2}$	$1=\frac{5}{5}$	$1=\frac{10}{10}$	$\frac{3}{5}+\frac{2}{5}=1$	$\frac{4}{5}+\frac{1}{5}=1$
I	$\frac{1}{10}+\frac{1}{10}=\frac{1}{5}$	$\frac{2}{10}+\frac{1}{10}=\frac{3}{10}$	$\frac{4}{10}+\frac{3}{10}=\frac{7}{10}$	$\frac{3}{10}+\frac{3}{10}=\frac{3}{5}$	$\frac{5}{10}+\frac{2}{10}=\frac{7}{10}$
J	$\frac{1}{2}=\frac{5}{10}$	$\frac{1}{5}=\frac{2}{10}$	$\frac{1}{2}+\frac{1}{5}=\frac{7}{10}$	$\frac{1}{2}+\frac{1}{10}=\frac{3}{5}$	$\frac{1}{5}+\frac{1}{10}=\frac{3}{10}$
K	$\frac{2}{5}=\frac{4}{10}$	$\frac{2}{5}+\frac{1}{10}=\frac{1}{2}$	$\frac{1}{2}+\frac{2}{5}=\frac{9}{10}$	$\frac{1}{2}+\frac{3}{10}=\frac{4}{5}$	$\frac{2}{5}+\frac{1}{10}=\frac{1}{2}$
L	$\frac{1}{5}-\frac{1}{10}=\frac{1}{10}$	$\frac{2}{5}-\frac{1}{10}=\frac{3}{10}$	$\frac{1}{2}-\frac{1}{5}=\frac{3}{10}$	$\frac{1}{2}-\frac{2}{5}=\frac{1}{10}$	$\frac{3}{5}-\frac{1}{2}=\frac{1}{10}$
M	$1-\frac{1}{2}=\frac{1}{2}$	$1-\frac{1}{5}=\frac{4}{5}$	$1-\frac{3}{5}=\frac{2}{5}$	$1-\frac{2}{5}=\frac{3}{5}$	$1-\frac{3}{10}=\frac{7}{10}$
N	$\frac{4}{5}-\frac{3}{10}=\frac{1}{2}$	$\frac{7}{10}-\frac{1}{2}=\frac{1}{5}$	$\frac{3}{10}-\frac{1}{5}=\frac{1}{10}$	$\frac{5}{10}-\frac{1}{2}=0$	$\frac{4}{5}-\frac{1}{2}=\frac{3}{10}$

Which is the greater?

O	$\frac{3}{10}$ or $\frac{1}{5}$	$\frac{3}{5}$ or $\frac{1}{2}$	$\frac{4}{10}$ or $\frac{1}{2}$	$\frac{4}{10}$ or $\frac{3}{5}$	$\frac{9}{10}$ or $\frac{4}{5}$
	$\frac{3}{10}$	$\frac{3}{5}$	$\frac{1}{2}$	$\frac{3}{5}$	$\frac{9}{10}$

A RAILWAY TIME TABLE

High Town *dep.*:	07.15	09.30	10.45	11.50	13.10	16.20	18.35	22.05
Near Town	07.23	09.40	10.52	11.58	13.18	16.26	18.44	22.12
Middle Town	07.36	09.53	11.04	12.12	13.32	16.38	18.58	22.24
Low Town	07.52	10.10	11.20	12.30	—	16.52	19.16	22.40
Far Town *arr.*:	08.05	10.25	11.32	12.45	—	17.04	19.30	22.52

Write answers to the following questions

A High Town *dep* : Far Town *arr*. Write in full the words represented by '*dep.*' and *arr.*'. departure, arrival

B Write in words the time at which the first train from High Town reaches Far Town. Five minutes past eight o'clock in the morning

C How long does it take the first train from High Town to reach Far Town? 50 minutes

D Which train leaves High Town before noon but arrives at Far Town after noon? The fourth, or 11.50 a.m.

E At what time does the first train leave High Town after noon to reach Far Town? 16.20

F Write down in the same order of the time table how long it takes for each morning train to travel from High Town to Far Town. 50 min., 55 min., 47 min., 55 min.

G Looking at your answers to the previous sum write down the time at which the fastest morning train leaves High Town. 10.45 a.m.

H Which is the fastest train from High Town to Near Town between 9 a.m. and Noon? 10.45 a.m.

I Which is the fastest train from Middle Town to Far Town after 16.00 hours? 16.20

J Which is the latest train you may catch at Near Town to reach Low Town before 16.00 hours? 11.58

K Suppose you live at Far Town and that it takes a quarter-hour to travel home from the station. At what time would you reach home if you left High Town by the last train of the day? 23.07

See notes on page 81.

Write answers only

A	67 sec. = 1 min. 7 sec.	75 sec. = 1 min. 15 sec.	96 sec. = 1 min. 36 sec.
B	72 min. = 1 hr. 12 min.	84 min. = 1 hr. 24 min.	98 min. = 1 hr. 38 min.
C	26 hr. = 1 day 2 hr.	30 hr. = 1 day 6 hr.	41 hr. = 1 day 17 hr.
D	48 hr. = 2 days 0 hr.	56 hr. = 2 days 8 hr.	64 hr. = 2 days 16 hr.
E	1 min. 12 sec. = 72 sec.	1 min. 22 sec. = 82 sec.	1 min. 35 sec. = 95 sec.
F	1 hr. 17 min. = 77 min.	1 hr. 27 min. = 87 min.	1 hr. 38 min. = 98 min.
G	1 day 8 hr. = 32 hr.	1 day 13 hr. = 37 hr.	1 day 22 hr. = 46 hr.

Add (+)

H

min.	sec.	min.	sec.	min.	sec.	min.	sec.	min.	sec.
1	12	2	31	1	40	4	49	12	55
1	23	1	9		52	11	8		40
1	27	3	24	1	30	7	37	6	38
4	2	7	4	4	2	23	34	20	13

I

hr.	min.	hr.	min.	hr.	min.	hr.	min.	hr.	min.
1	17	2	15	10	18	5	47	7	49
3	45		52	5	54	10	8	14	50
1	26	3	8	12	7	6	53		38
6	28	6	15	28	19	22	48	23	17

J

wk.	days	wk.	days	wk.	days	wk.	days	wk.	days
2	4	7	6	4	5	13	6	15	5
3	0		5	21	0	4	0		6
4	5	3	5	6	6		5	8	4
10	2	12	2	32	4	18	4	25	1

K

days	hr.	days	hr.	days	hr.	days	hr.	days	hr.
2	8	4	13	5	21	13	22	3	21
1	7	2	10	10	20	6	9	15	18
3	9	1	8	3	5		20	6	7
7	0	8	7	19	22	21	3	25	22

Subtract (−)

A

min. sec.	min. sec.	min. sec.	min. sec.	min. sec.
6 23	5 42	7 0	6 0	5 0
−2 18	−3 27	−4 15	−2 48	−1 36
4 5	2 15	2 45	3 12	3 24

B

min. sec.	min. sec.	min. sec.	min. sec.	min. sec.
4 15	6 26	15 17	12 32	25 40
−2 20	−3 44	−10 53	− 8 45	−16 48
1 55	2 42	4 24	3 47	8 52

C

hr. min.	hr. min.	hr. min.	hr. min.	hr. min.
3 16	6 21	5 16	8 32	10 0
−1 25	−4 36	−2 50	−4 47	− 9 23
1 51	1 45	2 26	3 45	37

D

wk. days	wk. days	wk. days	wk. days	wk. days
5 0	4 3	6 2	9 1	10 5
−2 5	−1 4	−5 4	−6 6	− 8 6
2 2	2 6	5	2 2	1 6

E

days hr.	days hr.	days hr.	days hr.	days hr.
6 2	5 10	7 15	6 21	9 18
−3 4	−2 16	−4 20	−2 23	−7 21
2 22	2 18	2 19	3 22	1 21

F

days hr.	days hr.	days hr.	days hr.	days hr.
4 9	7 0	10 8	9 16	12 15
−2 17	−6 19	−3 22	−8 18	−9 20
1 16	5	6 10	22	2 19

Work out these sums in your book

G What is the total time spent in school if morning school is from 8.55 a.m. to 12 noon, and afternoon school is from 1.25 p.m. to 4.00 p.m.? 5 hr. 40 min.

H In crossing the Atlantic Ocean a liner took 7 days 6 hours. The return crossing took 5 days 17 hrs. How much quicker was the return trip? 1 day 13 hr.

FRACTIONS

Write what part of these circles is shaded

A

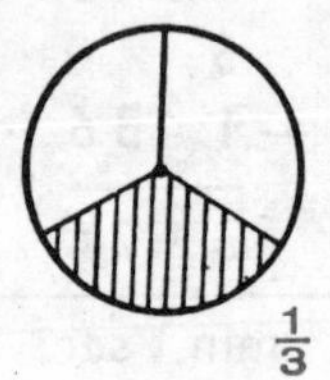

$\frac{1}{3}$

B

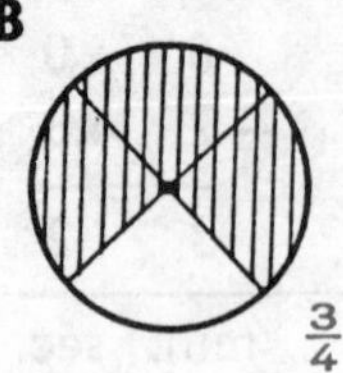

$\frac{3}{4}$

C

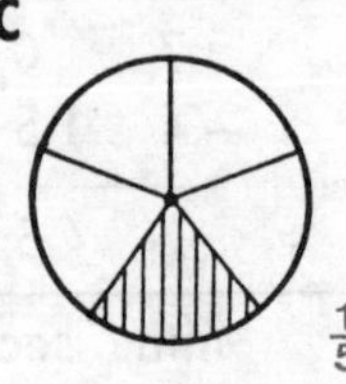

$\frac{1}{5}$

D

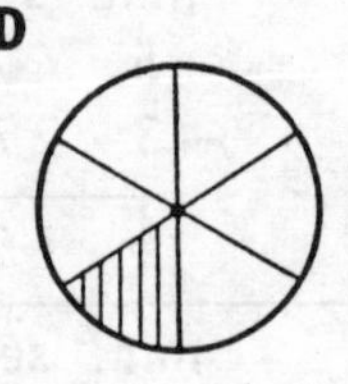

$\frac{1}{6}$

E

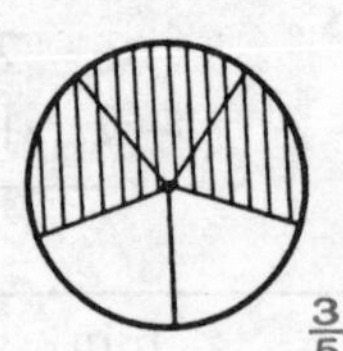

$\frac{3}{5}$

F How many halves in a whole one? 2

G How many halves in three whole ones? 6

H How many half-bars in five bars of chocolate? 10

I How many thirds in a whole one? 3

J How many thirds in two whole ones? 6

K How many third parts in four sticks of rock? 12

L How many quarters in two cakes? 8

M How many quarter apples in five apples? 20

N How many fifths in a whole one? 5

O How many fifth parts in three sticks of rock? 15

P How many fifth parts in six bars of chocolate? 30

Complete

Q	$\frac{1}{2}$ of £1 = 50p	$\frac{1}{4}$ of £1 = 25p	$\frac{1}{5}$ of £1 = 20p	$\frac{2}{5}$ of £1 = 40p
R	$\frac{1}{2}$ of 1 hour = 30 min.	$\frac{1}{4}$ of 1 min. = 15 sec.	$\frac{3}{4}$ of 1 min. = 45 sec.	$\frac{3}{4}$ of 12 = 9
S	$\frac{1}{3}$ of 1 hour = 20 min	$\frac{2}{3}$ of 1 hour = 40 min.	$\frac{2}{3}$ of 15 = 10	$\frac{2}{3}$ of 30p = 20p
T	$\frac{1}{5}$ of 20p = 4p	$\frac{2}{5}$ of 20p = 8p	$\frac{3}{5}$ of 40p = 24p	$\frac{4}{5}$ of 25p = 20p

Complete

A	$\frac{1}{2}$ of 10 = 5	$\frac{1}{2}$ of 18 = 9	$\frac{1}{2}$ of 32 = 16	$\frac{1}{4}$ of 16 = 4
B	$\frac{1}{4}$ of 12 = 3	$\frac{3}{4}$ of 12 = 9	$\frac{3}{4}$ of 16 = 12	$\frac{3}{4}$ of 20 = 15
C	$\frac{1}{4}$ of 36 = 9	$\frac{3}{4}$ of 36 = 27	$\frac{3}{4}$ of 8 = 6	$\frac{3}{4}$ of 40 = 30
D	$\frac{1}{3}$ of 6 = 2	$\frac{1}{3}$ of 12 = 4	$\frac{2}{3}$ of 12 = 8	$\frac{2}{3}$ of 15 = 10
E	$\frac{1}{3}$ of 21 = 7	$\frac{2}{3}$ of 21 = 14	$\frac{2}{3}$ of 18 = 12	$\frac{2}{3}$ of 30 = 20
F	$\frac{1}{8}$ of 16 = 2	$\frac{1}{8}$ of 24 = 3	$\frac{1}{8}$ of 40 = 5	$\frac{1}{8}$ of 48 = 6
G	$\frac{1}{8}$ of 32 = 4	$\frac{3}{8}$ of 32 = 12	$\frac{5}{8}$ of 32 = 20	$\frac{7}{8}$ of 32 = 28
H	$\frac{3}{8}$ of 24 = 9	$\frac{3}{8}$ of 40 = 15	$\frac{5}{8}$ of 56 = 35	$\frac{7}{8}$ of 64 = 56

I Divide (÷) Multiply (×)

$$4\,\overline{)\,£12\cdot68} = £3\cdot17$$

$$£3\cdot17 \times 3 = £9\cdot51$$

J What is $\frac{3}{4}$ of £12·68? £9·51

K	$\frac{1}{2}$ of £1·46 = £0·73	$\frac{1}{2}$ of 3·48 m = 1·74 m	$\frac{1}{2}$ of 7·68 l = 3·84 l
L	$\frac{1}{4}$ of £5·28 = £1·32	$\frac{3}{4}$ of £5·28 = £3·96	$\frac{3}{4}$ of £0·64 = £0·48
M	$\frac{1}{4}$ of £7·64 = £1·91	$\frac{3}{4}$ of £7·64 = £5·73	$\frac{3}{4}$ of £2·56 = £1·92
N	$\frac{1}{3}$ of 6·42 g = 2·14 g	$\frac{2}{3}$ of 6·42 g = 4·28 g	$\frac{2}{3}$ of 7·56 g = 5·04 g
O	$\frac{1}{5}$ of 7·65 m = 1·53 m	$\frac{2}{5}$ of 7·65 m = 3·06 m	$\frac{4}{5}$ of 7·65 m = 6·12 m

P $\frac{3}{8}$ of 1 hr. 20 min. = 30 min. $\frac{5}{8}$ of 1 hr. 20 min. = 50 min.

Q $\frac{2}{3}$ of 2 min. 45 sec. = 1 min. 50 sec. $\frac{3}{5}$ of 1 min. 40 sec. = 1 min.

Write what part of

R	1 hour are 20 minutes $\frac{1}{3}$	1 minute are 15 seconds $\frac{1}{4}$
S	1 minute are 45 seconds $\frac{3}{4}$	1 hour are 45 minutes $\frac{3}{4}$
T	1 hour are 40 minutes $\frac{2}{3}$	1 minute are 12 seconds $\frac{1}{5}$
U	2 hours are 30 minutes $\frac{1}{4}$	2 hours are 40 minutes $\frac{1}{3}$

THE FAMILY GROCER'S PRICE LIST

Bacon	23p per $\frac{1}{2}$ kg	Boiled Ham	10p per 100 grammes
Butter	21p per $\frac{1}{2}$ kg	Cheese	18p per $\frac{1}{2}$ kg
Cocoa	22p per tin	Corned Beef	24p per $\frac{1}{2}$ kg
	and $11\frac{1}{2}$p per tin	Coffee	$42\frac{1}{2}$p per tin
Currants	10p per $\frac{1}{2}$ kg		and 23p per tin
Eggs	2p each	Jam	$15\frac{1}{2}$p per 1 kg pot
Lard	14p per $\frac{1}{2}$ kg		and 8p per $\frac{1}{2}$ kg pot
Lemon Curd	$10\frac{1}{2}$p per pot	Margarine	12p per $\frac{1}{2}$ kg
Marmalade	$7\frac{1}{2}$p per pot	Minced Beef	$3\frac{1}{2}$p per 250 grammes
Mincemeat	10p per $\frac{1}{2}$ kg	Ox Tongue	11p per 100 grammes
Pressed Beef	7p per 100 grammes	Raisins	$11\frac{1}{2}$p per $\frac{1}{2}$ kg
Sugar	4p per $\frac{1}{2}$ kg	Sultanas	$9\frac{1}{2}$p per $\frac{1}{2}$ kg
Tea	42p per $\frac{1}{2}$ kg		

Say what change from a fifty should I receive if I buy

A	$\frac{1}{2}$ kg of bacon 27p	1 doz. eggs 26p	1 kg of cheese 14p
B	a large pot of jam $34\frac{1}{2}$p	200 g of Ox tongue 28p	a large tin of coffee $7\frac{1}{2}$p

Say what I should pay for $\frac{1}{4}$ kg of

C	bacon $11\frac{1}{2}$p	corned beef 12p	lard 7p
D	cheese 9p	raisins 6p	sultanas 5p
E	boiled ham 25p	minced beef $3\frac{1}{2}$p	ox-tongue $27\frac{1}{2}$p
F	pressed beef $17\frac{1}{2}$p	lemon curd $10\frac{1}{2}$p per pot	jam sold per $\frac{1}{2}$ kg pot

Say what I should pay for 1 kg of

G	cheese 36p	butter 42p	sugar 8p
H	corned beef 48p	sultanas 19p	mincemeat 20p

Say what I should pay for $\frac{1}{2}$ kg of

I	margarine 12p	boiled ham 50p	currants 10p
J	corned beef 24p	minced beef 7p	pressed beef 35p

Use the FAMILY GROCER'S PRICE LIST opposite

What change will there be from a fifty after paying either of these bills?

A

		p
Currants	$\frac{1}{2}$ kg	10
Raisins	$\frac{1}{2}$ kg	$11\frac{1}{2}$
Sultanas	1 kg	19
	total	$40\frac{1}{2}$p
	Change	$9\frac{1}{2}$p

B

		p
Jam	1 kg	$15\frac{1}{2}$
Marmalade	1 pot	$7\frac{1}{2}$
Sugar	$1\frac{1}{2}$ kg	12
	total	35p
	Change	15p

What change will there be from seven tens after paying either of these bills?

C

		p
Bacon	$\frac{3}{4}$ kg	$34\frac{1}{2}$
Lard	$\frac{3}{4}$ kg	21
Pressed beef	200 g	14
	total	$69\frac{1}{2}$p
	Change	$\frac{1}{2}$p

D

		p
Tea	$\frac{1}{4}$ kg	21
Coffee—small		23
Cocoa—large		22
	total	66p
	Change	4p

What change will there be from a one pound note after paying either of these bills?

E

		p
Jam	$1\frac{1}{2}$ kg	$23\frac{1}{2}$
Margarine	$\frac{1}{4}$ kg	6
Ox tongue	200 g	22
Minced beef	$\frac{1}{2}$ kg	7
Butter	$\frac{3}{4}$ kg	$31\frac{1}{2}$
Eggs	4	8
	total	98p
	Change	2p

F

		p
Currants	1 kg	20
Raisins	$\frac{1}{4}$ kg	6
Sultanas	$\frac{1}{2}$ kg	$9\frac{1}{2}$
Lemon curd	2 pots	21
Tea	$\frac{1}{4}$ kg	21
Boiled ham	200 g	20
	total	$97\frac{1}{2}$p
	Change	$2\frac{1}{2}$p

See notes on page 81.

PLACE VALUE

Write the value in words and in figures of the 1 in each number

A	1 350	one thousand,	1 000
B	2 134	one hundred,	100
C	4 010	one ten,	10
D	6 701	one unit,	1
E	9 010	one ten,	10
F	6 184	one hundred,	100
G	1 578	one thousand,	1 000

Notice: From A to D at each step the figure 1 moves one place to the right.
From D to G at each step the figure 1 moves one place to the left.

H As the place of a figure is changed to the right does the value increase or does the value decrease? decrease

I As the place of a figure is changed to the left does the value increase or does it decrease? increase

J How many times greater is the 1 in C than that in D? 10

K How many times less is the 1 in D than that in C? 10

L How many times less is the 1 in E than that in F? 10

M How many times less is the 1 in D than that in B? 100

N How many times less is the 1 in D than that in A? 1 000

O How many times less is the 7 in G than that in D? 10

Complete

P To move a figure one place to the right makes it 10 times smaller.

Q To move a figure two places to the right makes it 100 times smaller.

R To move a figure three places to the right makes it 1 000 times smaller.

S To move a figure three places to the left makes it 1 000 times bigger.

T To move a figure one place to the left makes it 10 times bigger.

U How many times greater is the value of the 3 in A than that in B? 10

V How many times less is the value of the 4 in B than that in C? 1 000

A Write in words: 0·01 nought point nought one; one hundredth.

B Write in words: 0·1 nought point one; one tenth.

C How many hundredths in 0·1? 10 0·2? 20 0·5? 50

D How many hundredths in 0·11? 11 0·21? 21 0·51? 51
0·23? 23 0·67? 67 0·09? 9

E Write in words: 0·1 nought point one; one tenth 1·0 one

F How many tenths in 1? 10 2? 20 3? 30 7? 70
1·1? 11 2·1? 21 3·4? 34 7·6? 76

G How many hundredths in 0·01? 1 0·1? 10 1·0? 100
0·23? 23 0·4? 40 1·1? 110

H How many tenths in 0·7? 7 1·7? 17 0·17? 1 0·07? 0

I How many hundredths in 0·4? 40 0·04? 4 1·04? 104 0·44? 44

Write these numbers in figures

J 1 unit and 3 tenths 1·3 one tenth and three hundredths 0·13

K three hundredths 0·03 five tenths and six hundredths 0·56

L seven hundredths 0·07 twenty-four hundredths 0·24

M fifteen tenths 1·5 forty-seven hundredths 0·47

N fifty-six tenths 5·6 thirty-eight hundredths 0·38

Complete

O 0·08 + 0·03 = 0·11 0·07 + 0·04 = 0·11 0·07 + 0·06 = 0·13

P 0·06 + 0·08 = 0·14 0·17 + 0·05 = 0·22 0·19 + 0·03 = 0·22

Q 0·27 + 0·05 = 0·32 0·36 + 0·07 = 0·43 0·58 + 0·06 = 0·64

R 0·8 + 0·6 = 1·4 0·7 + 0·8 = 1·5 0·6 + 0·16 = 0·76

S 0·7 + 0·8 = 1·5 1·8 + 0·5 = 2·3 2·7 + 0·5 = 3·2

DECIMALS

A What is the value of a figure one place to the right of units? tenths

B What is the value of a figure one place to the right of tenths? hundredths

C What do you think we call the place value of figures to the right of hundredths? thousandths

If we make hundreds ten times greater we have thousands.
If we make hundredths ten times less we have thousandths.
We show thousandths by "th"
Look at this number:

Th	H	T	U ·	t	h	th
3	2	7	5 ·	8	4	9

State the place value in words of the figures

D	2	hundreds	5	units	4	hundredths
E	3	thousands	8	tenths	9	thousandths

How many thousandths in

F	0·006	6	0·016	16	0·008	8	0·018	18	0·028	28
G	0·043	43	0·143	143	0·243	243	0·627	627	0·081	81
H	0·027	27	0·207	207	0·516	516	0·82	820	0·93	930

Complete

I	0·008 + 0·004 = 0·012	0·009 + 0·003 = 0·012	0·007 + 0·005 = 0·012
J	0·006 + 0·009 = 0·015	0·007 + 0·008 = 0·015	0·018 + 0·003 = 0·021
K	0·017 + 0·006 = 0·023	0·018 + 0·005 = 0·023	0·016 + 0·004 = 0·02

Write these numbers in figures

L	two thousandths 0·002	four hundredths and six thousandths 0·046
M	twenty-two thousandths 0·022	six tenths and five thousandths 0·605
N	seventeen hundredths 0·17	eight tenths and three hundredths 0·83
O	nineteen thousandths 0·019	seven hundredths and four thousandths 0·074

MILLI

We have a special way of showing thousandths when measuring.
One thousandth of a metre we call a millimetre.
One thousandth of a gramme we call a milligramme.
One thousandth of a litre we call a millilitre.

State how many millimetres there are in

A	0·007 metre	7	0·023 metre	23	0·067 metre	67	0·081 metre	81
B	0·032 metre	32	0·132 metre	132	0·216 metre	216	0·207 metre	207

State how many millilitres there are in

C	0·026 litre	26	0·145 litre	145	0·39 litre	390	0·68 litre	680

State how many milligrammes there are in

D	0·304 gramme	304	0·52 gramme	520	0·5 gramme	500	0·8 gramme	800

Complete

E 1·006 metre = 1 m 6 mm   1·062 litre = 1 l 62 ml
F 1·081 gramme = 1 g 81 mg   1·08 gramme = 1 g 80 mg
G 2·05 litre = 2 l 50 ml   3·5 metre = 3 m 500 mm
H 1·08 metre = 1 m 80 mm   2·8 litre = 2 l 800 ml
I To change millimetres to metres we shall divide by 1,000.
J To change milligrammes to grammes we shall make the number 1,000 times less.
K To change millilitres to litres we shall move the figure three places to the right and write the number as a decimal.

L	1,000 mm = 1 m	119 mg = 0·119 g	423 ml = 0·423 l
M	1,706 ml = 1·706 l	706 mm = 0·706 m	76 ml = 0·076 l
N	607 mg = 0·607 g	600 ml = 0·6 l	800 mm = 0·8 m
O	400 mm = 0·4 m	40 mm = 0·04 m	70 mg = 0·07 g
P	90 ml = 0·09 l	9 mm = 0·009 m	7 mm = 0·007 m
Q	1,007 mg = 1·007 g	3,070 ml = 3·07 l	5,500 mm = 5·5 m

Complete

A To multiply by 1 000 we move figures 3 places to the left.

B To divide by 1 000 we move figures 3 places to the right.

C	1 litre = 1 000 millilitres	0·5 litre = 500 millilitres	
D	1 metre = 1 000 millimetres	0·3 metre = 300 millimetres	
E	$\frac{1}{2}$ metre = 500 millimetres	$\frac{1}{2}$ litre = 500 millilitres	
F	0·234 m = 234 mm	0·306 g = 306 mg	0·278 g = 278 mg
G	0·86 l = 860 ml	0·73 l = 730 ml	0·69 l = 690 ml
H	0·075 m = 75 mm	0·032 m = 32 mm	0·048 m = 48 mm
I	1 litre = 1 000 ml	$\frac{1}{2}$ litre = 500 ml	$1\frac{1}{2}$ litres = 1 500 ml
J	1 metre = 1 000 mm	$\frac{1}{2}$ metre = 500 mm	$\frac{1}{4}$ metre = 250 mm
K	$\frac{1}{4}$ litre = 250 ml	$\frac{3}{4}$ litre = 750 ml	$\frac{1}{5}$ metre = 200 mm
L	0·706 m = 706 mm	0·37 litre = 370 ml	0·008 l = 8 ml
M	0·07 l = 70 ml	0·006 l = 6 ml	0·07 m = 70 mm
N	0·6 l = 600 ml	0·4 m = 400 mm	0·9 g = 900 mg
O	1 000 mm = 1 m	100 mm = 0·1 m	10 mm = 0·01 m
P	1 000 ml = 1 l	245 ml = 0·245 l	45 ml = 0·045 l
Q	1 000 mg = 1 g	307 mg = 0·307 g	48 mg = 0·048 g
R	356 ml = 0·356 l	56 ml = 0·056 l	93 ml = 0·093 l
S	409 mm = 0·409 m	9 mm = 0·009 m	6 mm = 0·006 m
T	560 mm = 0·56 m	870 ml = 0·87 l	240 mg = 0·24 g
U	400 mg = 0·4 g	600 mm = 0·6 m	800 ml = 0·8 l
V	208 ml = 0·208 l	8 ml = 0·008 l	7 mm = 0·007 m
W	90 mm = 0·09 m	9 mm = 0·009 m	5 ml = 0·005 l
X	700 mg = 0·7 g	50 mm = 0·05 m	300 mm = 0·3 m

Measure these lines and state your answer first as millimetres and then as centimetres and millimetres

A ________________ 35 mm, 3 cm 5 mm

B __________________________________ 77 mm, 7 cm 7 mm

C _______________________ 52 mm, 5 cm 2 mm

Write as decimals in centimetres

D	1 cm 3 mm	1·3	1 cm 6 mm	1·6	2 cm 1 mm	2·1	1 cm 8 mm	1·8
E	3 cm 5 mm	3·5	2 cm 4 mm	2·4	1 cm 9 mm	1·9	3 cm 7 mm	3·7

Write in centimetres and millimetres

F	1·2 cm	1 cm 2 mm	2·8 cm	2 cm 8 mm	3·2 cm	3 cm 2mm	1·5 cm	1 cm 5 mm
G	2·9 cm	2 cm 9 mm	4·3 cm	4 cm 3 mm	1·7 cm	1 cm 7 mm	5·6 cm	5 cm 6 mm

---

Write as centimetres

H	1·25 m	125	0·25 m	25	0·64 m	64	0·57 cm	57
I	0·5 m	50	1·5 m	150	0·08 m	8	0·09 m	9

Write as millimetres

J	1 m	1 000	1·327 m	1 327	0·357 m	357	0·307 m	307
K	0·261 m	261	0·061 m	61	0·082 m	82	0·82 m	820
L	0·76 m	760	0·8 m	800	0·9 m	900	0·09 m	90

Complete

M	1 l = 1 000 ml	1·236 l = 1 236 ml	0·236 l = 236 ml
N	1 g = 1 000 mg	0·348 g = 348 mg	0·609 g = 609 mg
O	0·286 g = 286 mg	0·086 g = 86 mg	1·086 g = 1 086 mg
P	0·329 g = 329 mg	1·029 g = 1 029 mg	1·02 g = 1 020 mg
Q	1·607 g = 1 607 mg	1·007 l = 1 007 ml	0·009 l = 9 ml
R	1·046 l = 1 046 ml	2·006 l = 2 006 ml	1·66 l = 1 660 ml
S	1·37 m = 1 370 mm	1·3 m = 1 300 mm	1·7 m = 1 700 mm
T	2·8 g = 2 800 mg	1·08 g = 1 080 mg	0·008 l = 8 ml

METRES, LITRES and GRAMMES

Complete

A To change metres to centimetres we multiply by 100 .
B To change centimetres to millimetres we multiply by 10 .
C To change litres to millilitres we multiply by 1 000 .
D To change grammes to milligrammes we multiply by 1 000 .
E To change millimetres to centimetres we divide by 10 .
F To change centimetres to metres we divide by 100 .
G To change millimetres to metres we divide by 1 000 .
H To change millilitres to litres we divide by 1 000 .

Write as decimals in centimetres

I **1 cm 4 mm** 1·4 **1 cm 7 mm** 1·7 **9 mm** 0·9 **5 cm 8 mm** 5·8 **6 mm** 0·6

Write as decimals in metres

J	**1 m 37 cm** 1·37	**1 m 40 cm** 1·4	**2 m 76 cm** 2·76	**1 m 80 cm** 1·8
K	**1 m 30 cm** 1·3	**1 m 3 cm** 1·03	**1 m 8 cm** 1·08	**2 m 6 cm** 2·06
L	**3 m 96 cm** 3·96	**98 cm** 0·98	**70 cm** 0·7	**9 cm** 0·09
M	**1 m 20 cm** 1·2	**60 cm** 0·6	**6 cm** 0·06	**8 cm** 0·08

Write as decimal quantities of metres, litres or grammes

N	**1 m 342 mm=**1·342 m	**1 m 765 mm=**1·765 m	**1 m 806 mm=**1·806 m
O	**1 l 255 ml =**1·255 l	**2 l 305 ml =**2·305 l	**1 l 350 ml =**1·35 l
P	**1 g 750 mg =**1·75 g	**1 g 800 mg =**1·8 g	**1 g 600 mg =**1·6 g
Q	**855 mg =**0·855 g	**607 ml =**0·607 l	**905 mm=**0·905 m
R	**950 mm=**0·95 m	**620 mm=**0·62 m	**600 mm=**0·6 m
S	**400 ml =**0·4 l	**200 ml =**0·2 l	**20 ml =**0·02 l
T	**70 mm=**0·07m	**90 mg =**0·09 g	**80 ml =**0·08 l
U	**500 ml =**0·5 l	**50 mm=**0·05 m	**5 mm=**0·005 m

GENERAL REVISION

Write answers only. Work across the page

A	$7 \times 6 = 42$	$7 \times 8 = 56$	$8 \times 9 = 72$	$6 \times 9 = 54$	$5 \times 12 = 60$
B	$16 + 5 = 21$	$12 - 7 = 5$	$13 - 8 = 5$	$14 + 7 = 21$	$23 + 8 = 31$
C	$40 \div 8 = 5$	$51 \div 7 = 7r2$	$9 \times 8 = 72$	$9 \times 9 = 81$	$7 \times 12 = 84$
D	$10 \times 10 = 100$	$12 \times 8 = 96$	$7 \times 9 = 63$	$21 - 6 = 15$	$43 + 7 = 50$
E	$17 + 6 = 23$	$18 - 10 = 8$	$8 \times 8 = 64$	$12 \times 9 = 108$	$19 - 10 = 9$
F	$60 \div 7 = 8r4$	$74 \div 9 = 8r2$	$80 \div 12 = 6r8$	$91 \div 8 = 11r3$	$110 \div 12 = 9r2$

Complete

G	60p + 45p = £1·05	73p + 42p = £1·15	56p + 48p = £1·04
H	71p + 59p = £1·30	86p + 57p = £1·43	78p + 39p = £1·17
I	80p − 73p = 7p	70p − 64p = 6p	50p − 22p = 28p
J	50p − 36p = 14p	90p − 81p = 9p	100p − 75p = 25p
K	£1 − 28p = 72p	£1 − 66p = 34p	£1 − 43p = 57p

L $\frac{1}{2}$ hr. after 12 noon is 12.30 p.m. 40 min. before 12 noon is 11.20 a.m.

M 12 hr. after 2.30 p.m. is 2.30 a.m. 12 hr. before 4.50 p.m. is 4.50 a.m.

N $\frac{1}{2}$ of 2 hr. 30 min. = 1 hr. 15 min. $\frac{3}{4}$ of 1 hr. 20 min. = 1 hr.

O	$\frac{1}{3}$ of 27 = 9	$\frac{2}{3}$ of 27 = 18	$\frac{1}{5}$ of 60 = 12	$\frac{3}{5}$ of 35 = 21
P	$\frac{5}{6}$ of 48 = 40	$\frac{1}{8}$ of 96 = 12	$\frac{3}{8}$ of 56 = 21	$\frac{7}{8}$ of 72 = 63

Subtract (−)

Q

$$\begin{array}{r} 6211 \\ -\ 5218 \\ \hline 993 \end{array} \qquad \begin{array}{r} 7006 \\ -\ 909 \\ \hline 6097 \end{array}$$

Multiply (×)

R

$$\begin{array}{r} 2006 \\ \times\ 7 \\ \hline 14042 \end{array} \qquad \begin{array}{r} 4089 \\ \times\ 12 \\ \hline 49068 \end{array} \qquad \begin{array}{r} 405 \\ \times\ 20 \\ \hline 8100 \end{array}$$

Add (+)

S

$$\begin{array}{r} 4305 \\ 680 \\ 5079 \\ 836 \\ \hline 10900 \end{array} \qquad \begin{array}{r} 6874 \\ 96 \\ 509 \\ 68 \\ \hline 7547 \end{array}$$

Multiply (×)

T

$$\begin{array}{r} 134 \\ \times\ 16 \\ \hline 2144 \end{array} \qquad \begin{array}{r} 507 \\ \times\ 23 \\ \hline 11661 \end{array} \qquad \begin{array}{r} 860 \\ \times\ 35 \\ \hline 30100 \end{array}$$

Divide (÷)

U

$$6\overline{)403} = 67r1 \qquad 7\overline{)1010} = 144r2 \qquad 9\overline{)8001} = 889 \qquad 11\overline{)2090} = 190 \qquad 12\overline{)1190} = 99r2$$

GENERAL REVISION

A If 1st July was on Thursday give the dates of these days in that week:
Saturday 3rd July Wednesday 30th June Monday 28th June

B Which of these will be Leap Years? 1976 1980 1990 1976; 1980

C How many days are there from 25th May to 4th June? 10

Add (+)

D

£12·64	9·3 cm
£ 5·08	10·8 cm
£40·96	0·7 cm
£58·68	20·8 cm

Subtract (−)

E

£5·06	£3·80	5·62 m
− £3·86	− £0·93	− 2·83 m
£1·20	£2·87	2·79 m

Multiply (×)

F

$38\frac{1}{2}$p	£4·05	£1·80$\frac{1}{2}$	£2·08$\frac{1}{2}$	£4·09
× 7	× 8	× 11	× 5	× 12
$269\frac{1}{2}$p	£32·40	£19·85$\frac{1}{2}$	£10·42$\frac{1}{2}$	£49·08

Divide (÷)

G

9)£18·54 = £2·06 8)£2·74 = £0·34 r2p 7)£10·04 = £1·43 r3p 12)£30·08 = £2·50$\frac{1}{2}$ r2p 11)£4·50 = £0·40$\frac{1}{2}$ r4$\frac{1}{2}$p

How many thousandths in

H 0·004 4 0·007 7 0·017 17 0·063 63 0·163 163 0·204 204

Write in figures

I five hundredths 0·05 fifteen thousandths 0·015 nine thousandths 0·009

Complete

J	409 mm = 0·409 m	650 cm = 6·5 m	73 mm = 7·3 cm
K	200 mm = 20 cm	301 mm = 30·1 cm	301 mm = 0·301 m
L	300 ml = 0·3 l	750 mg = 0·75 g	1 900 ml = 1·9 l
M	0·623 m = 62·3 cm	0·623 m = 623 mm	0·086 l = 86 ml

REVISION OF NUMBER

Write answers only

A	5+3= 8	8− 5= 3	9− 4= 5	5+ 4= 9	7+3= 10
B	11−5= 6	6+ 5= 11	8+ 7= 15	15− 7= 8	13−8= 5
C	3×4= 12	7× 2= 14	12÷ 6= 2	18÷ 3= 6	21÷7= 3
D	14+7= 21	15− 6= 9	24÷ 8= 3	6× 7= 42	9×8= 72
E	27÷9= 3	28÷ 4= 7	16+ 8= 24	18− 9= 9	7×8= 56
F	12×3= 36	36÷ 9= 4	42÷ 7= 6	11× 7= 77	48÷6= 8
G	54÷9= 6	8×12= 96	24+ 7= 31	56÷ 8= 7	63÷7= 9
H	33−7= 26	72÷ 9= 8	108÷12= 9	11×12= 132	106÷9= 11 r7

Subtract (−)

I	5602	4384	6512	4432	5093
	− 804	− 395	− 505	−3997	− 998
	4798	3989	6007	435	4095

Add (+)

J	1898	1421	2324	1536	3114	5232
	2905	2308	1643	3053	659	698
	2587	1897	4788	968	875	9075
	1598	3699	1579	2988	4787	856
	8988	9325	10334	8545	9435	15861

Subtract (−)

K	2006	5000	4793	8062	6002
	−1807	−4996	−3695	− 994	− 599
	199	4	1098	7068	5403

Multiply (×)

L	788	509	879	3080	5098	6089
	× 9	× 12	× 11	× 7	× 11	× 12
	7092	6108	9669	21560	56078	73068

Divide (÷)

M	1167	887	97	689r7	975
	6)7002	8)7096	11)1067	9)6208	12)11700

Write answers only

A In each of seven drums are five litres of oil. How many litres of oil are there altogether? 35 litres

B A farmer has sheep in three fields. In the first are 28, in the second are 9 and in the third are 7. How many sheep has the farmer altogether? 44 sheep

C Jim began a game with 23 marbles but lost 8. How many marbles had Jim at the end of the game? 15 marbles

D Father is to plant two score cabbages. How many rows will there be if he puts 8 in each row? 5 rows

E What is one-seventh of fifty-six? 8

F How many $\frac{1}{2}$ litre tins can be filled from ten litres of paint? 20 tins

Work out these sums in your book

G From Monday to Friday the milkman delivered 268 bottles of milk daily. How many was that altogether? 1 340 bottles

H There should be 324 children at school, but there are only 286 present. How many children are absent? 38 absent

I An aeroplane flies for seven hours at a steady speed of 348 km.p.h. How far does it travel? 2 436 kilometres

J If a plane has to travel 2 904 kilometres in eight hours, at what steady speed in km.p.h. must it fly? 363 km.p.h.

K A farmer has two-hundred-and-sixty-three sheep and decides to reduce the flock by one-hundred-and-seventy-five. How many sheep will the farmer have then? 88 sheep

L A poultry farmer had six-hundred-and-ninety-eight head of poultry and decides to increase the flock by two-hundred-and-seventy-five. What head of poultry will he have then? 973 head of poultry

M What number is equal to one-ninth of 3 231? 359

N If we reduce five-hundred-and-fifty-two by one-eighth what will be the new number? 483

SPEED PRACTICE

Multiply (×)

A	5× 6=30	7× 4= 28	10× 3=30	12× 2= 24	4× 9= 36
B	3×12=36	8× 5= 40	4×11=44	9× 6= 54	4×12= 48
C	6× 8=48	7× 8= 56	6×10=60	11× 7= 77	12× 5= 60
D	8× 8=64	9× 7= 63	10× 8= 80	12× 6= 72	7×12= 84
E	7× 9=63	12× 8= 96	11× 9=99	10×11=110	12× 9=108
F	9× 8=72	10×12=120	9× 9=81	12×12=144	11×12=132

Multiply (×)

G	123 × 10 = 1230	305 × 10 = 3050	234 × 20 = 4680	506 × 20 = 10120
H	340 × 10 = 3400	670 × 10 = 6700	230 × 20 = 4600	170 × 40 = 6800
I	125 × 20 = 2500	204 × 50 = 10200	105 × 40 = 4200	306 × 50 = 15300
J	123 × 21 = 2583	216 × 21 = 4536	152 × 31 = 4712	217 × 22 = 4774
K	164 × 23 = 3772	217 × 32 = 6944	232 × 16 = 3712	254 × 24 = 6096

G–I Multipliers are multiples of 10 with noughts difficulties.
J–K Two-stage multiplying without noughts difficulties.

Multiply (×)

A	206 × 23 4738	107 × 31 3317	306 × 14 4284	208 × 24 4992
B	230 × 21 4830	140 × 23 3220	270 × 32 8640	160 × 17 2720
C	135 × 32 4320	245 × 32 7840	126 × 25 3150	144 × 25 3600
D	235 × 23 5405	145 × 24 3480	325 × 42 13650	216 × 25 5400
E	305 × 33 10065	205 × 23 4715	105 × 24 2520	406 × 25 10150
F	205 × 26 5330	472 × 23 10856	308 × 15 4620	505 × 24 12120
G	135 × 28 3780	307 × 32 9824	294 × 35 10290	405 × 26 10530

Continuing harder examples with noughts difficulties.

Multiply (×)

A	453 × 22 = 9966	578 × 32 = 18496	496 × 42 = 20832	387 × 34 = 13158
B	305 × 18 = 5490	408 × 35 = 14280	379 × 26 = 9854	480 × 35 = 16800
C	260 × 35 = 9100	506 × 25 = 12650	408 × 52 = 21216	687 × 29 = 19923

Work out these sums in your book

D At a sports ground are 23 rows of seats, having 118 seats in each row. How many seats are there altogether? 2 714

E A builder needed 575 blue bricks for each of 24 houses. How many blue bricks must be ordered? 13 800

F What number is fifteen times larger than two-hundred-and-seven? 3 105

G Find the product of three-hundred-and-forty-six and sixteen. 5 536

H What number equals twenty-four times five-hundred-and-eight? 12 192

I If a machine can fill 138 paper bags each hour, how many should it fill in seventeen hours? 2 346

J A school is open for twenty-three days during the month. On each day 345 bottles of milk were delivered. What was the total number of bottles delivered to the school that month? 7 935

K An aeroplane can fly at a steady speed of 325 km.p.h. If it could be kept flying for a whole day how far would it travel? 7 800 kilometres

A–C Harder examples.

How much must Mother pay to each tradesman?

Dr. to Mr. Baker

		p
5 loaves of white bread @ $5\frac{1}{2}$p per loaf	=	$27\frac{1}{2}$
7 loaves of brown bread @ $4\frac{1}{2}$p per loaf	=	$31\frac{1}{2}$
6 swiss rolls @ $1\frac{1}{2}$p each	=	9
Total		68p

Dr. to Mr. Coalman

		£
2 kilos of coal @ £1·25 per kilo	=	2·50
$1\frac{1}{2}$ kilos of coke @ £1·14 per kilo	=	1·71
1 sack of logs @ 29p per sack	=	0·29
Total		£4·50

Dr. to Mr. Milkman

		£
6 litres of milk @ $8\frac{1}{2}$p per litre	=	0·51
$1\frac{1}{2}$ kg of butter @ 39p per kg	=	$0{\cdot}58\frac{1}{2}$
6 eggs @ $2\frac{1}{2}$p each	=	0·15
Total		$£1{\cdot}24\frac{1}{2}$

Dr. to Mr. Greengrocer

		p
$3\frac{1}{2}$ kg of new potatoes @ 10p per kg	=	35
$\frac{1}{2}$ kg of carrots @ 9p per kg	=	$4\frac{1}{2}$
2 lettuces @ $6\frac{1}{2}$p each	=	13
$1\frac{1}{2}$ kg of apples @ 15p per kg	=	$22\frac{1}{2}$
Total		75p

Dr. to Mr. Butcher

		£
3 kg of beef @ $53\frac{1}{2}$p per kg	=	$1{\cdot}60\frac{1}{2}$
$\frac{1}{2}$ kg of minced meat @ 35p per kg	=	$0{\cdot}17\frac{1}{2}$
$\frac{1}{2}$ kg of sausages @ 37p per kg	=	$0{\cdot}18\frac{1}{2}$
$2\frac{1}{2}$ kg of pork @ 49p per kg	=	$1{\cdot}22\frac{1}{2}$
Total		£3·19

How much must Mother pay altogether? $£10{\cdot}93\frac{1}{2}$

See notes on page 82.

KILOS

Complete

A To make a number ten times greater we move the figures 1 place to the left .

B To make a number one thousand times greater we move the figures 3 places to the left .

Change to metres, litres or grammes

C	1 kilometre = 1 000 metres	$\frac{1}{2}$ kilolitre = 500 litres	
D	$\frac{1}{2}$ kilogramme = 500 grammes	$\frac{1}{4}$ kilometre = 250 metres	
E	0·1 km = 100 m	0·2 kl = 200 l	0·3 kg = 300 g
F	0·236 kg = 236 g	0·304 km = 304 m	0·756 kl = 756 l
G	0·562 km = 562 m	0·56 km = 560 m	0·82 kg = 820 g
H	0·63 kg = 630 g	0·6 kg = 600 g	0·7 kl = 700 l
I	0·802 kl = 802 l	0·8 kl = 800 l	0·5 km = 500 m
J	0·02 kg = 20 g	0·06 km = 60 m	0·037 kg = 37 g
K	0·008 kl = 8 l	0·009 kg = 9 g	0·006 kl = 6 l
L	0·09 km = 90 m	0·004 kl = 4 l	0·9 km = 900 m

Write as kilos and metres, litres or grammes

M	1·125 kg = 1 kg 125 g	2·763 kl = 2 kl 763 l
N	1·708 km = 1 km 708 m	3·75 kg = 3 kg 750 g
O	3·95 kl = 3 kl 950 l	2·084 km = 2 km 84 m
P	1·073 kg = 1 kg 73 g	4·08 kl = 4 kl 80 l
Q	2·01 km = 2 km 10 m	7·09 kg = 7 kg 90 g
R	4·7 kl = 4 kl 700 l	3·8 km = 3 km 800 m
S	10·09 kg = 10 kg 90 g	6·5 kl = 6 kl 500 l

KILOS

Complete

A To change centimetres to metres we divide by 100 , which means moving the figures 2 places to the right .

B To change grammes to kilogrammes we divide by 1 000 , which means moving the figures 3 places to the right .

Change to kilos, stating all answers as decimals

C	1 000 l = 1 kl	500 m = 0·5 km	500 g = 0·5 kg
D	600 m = 0·6 km	607 l = 0·607 kl	640 g = 0·64 kg
E	308 g = 0·308 kg	901 m = 0·901 km	708 m = 0·708 km
F	200 g = 0·2 kg	20 l = 0·02 kl	60 l = 0·06 kl
G	90 m = 0·09 km	40 g = 0·04 kg	4 m = 0·004 km
H	8 l = 0·008 kl	9 m = 0·009 km	7 l = 0·007 kl
I	50 g = 0·05 kg	700 l = 0·7 kl	650 g = 0·65 kg
J	9 g = 0·009 kg	80 g = 0·08 kg	800 m = 0·8 km

Which is the greater or the greatest?

K 0·8 m or 0·80 m Same   0·07 l or 0·070 l Same   1·5 kg or 1·500 kg Same

L 2·005 km, 2·050 km or 2·500 km   2·500 km

Change to kilos, stating all answers as decimals

M	1 kg 576 g = 1·576 kg	2 kg 306 g = 2·306 kg	1 km 406 m = 1·406 km
N	2 kl 570 l = 2·57 kl	1 kl 680 l = 1·68 kl	2 km 190 m = 2·19 km
O	1 km 600 m = 1·6 km	3 km 300 m = 3·3 km	1 kg 900 g = 1·9 kg
P	2 kg 60 g = 2·06 kg	1 kg 80 g = 1·08 kg	3 kl 70 l = 3·07 kl
Q	3 kl 6 l = 3·006 kl	2 kl 9 l = 2·009 kl	1 km 8 m = 1·008 km
R	1 km 5 m = 1·005 km	3 km 40 m = 3·04 km	5 kg 90 g = 5·09 kg
S	2 kg 300 g = 2·3 kg	1 kl 30 l = 1·03 kl	4 km 7 m = 4·007 km

Write answers only. Work across the page

A	$0.2 \times 4 = 0.8$	$0.3 \times 4 = 1.2$	$0.6 \times 4 = 2.4$	$0.6 \times 5 = 3$
B	$0.5 \times 2 = 1$	$0.4 \times 5 = 2$	$0.5 \times 6 = 3$	$0.5 \times 8 = 4$
C	$1.2 \times 3 = 3.6$	$1.2 \times 7 = 8.4$	$0.8 \times 7 = 5.6$	$0.7 \times 9 = 6.3$
D	$0.03 \times 3 = 0.09$	$0.03 \times 4 = 0.12$	$0.06 \times 4 = 0.24$	$0.08 \times 7 = 0.56$
E	$0.14 \times 3 = 0.42$	$0.17 \times 5 = 0.85$	$0.05 \times 6 = 0.3$	$0.08 \times 5 = 0.4$
F	$0.8 \times 9 = 7.2$	$0.5 \times 12 = 6$	$0.25 \times 8 = 2$	$0.15 \times 12 = 1.8$

Multiply (×)

G	$2.4 \times 2 = 4.8$	$3.5 \times 3 = 10.5$	$5.6 \times 6 = 33.6$	$4.7 \times 8 = 37.6$	$6.9 \times 7 = 48.3$	$5.8 \times 9 = 52.2$
H	$1.14 \times 4 = 4.56$	$2.37 \times 5 = 11.85$	$1.68 \times 6 = 10.08$	$2.07 \times 5 = 10.35$	$1.09 \times 8 = 8.72$	$2.07 \times 9 = 18.63$
I	$1.5 \times 2 = 3$	$3.5 \times 4 = 14$	$2.6 \times 5 = 13$	$4.8 \times 5 = 24$	$5.6 \times 5 = 28$	$4.5 \times 12 = 54$
J	$0.16 \times 4 = 0.64$	$0.23 \times 6 = 1.38$	$0.47 \times 5 = 2.35$	$0.06 \times 5 = 0.3$	$0.05 \times 8 = 0.4$	$0.75 \times 12 = 9$
K	$0.008 \times 4 = 0.032$	$0.016 \times 6 = 0.096$	$0.037 \times 8 = 0.296$	$0.065 \times 8 = 0.52$	$0.045 \times 12 = 0.54$	
L	$1.127 \times 8 = 9.016$	$1.216 \times 7 = 8.512$	$1.069 \times 9 = 9.621$	$0.786 \times 11 = 8.646$	$1.809 \times 12 = 21.708$	

DIVISION OF DECIMALS

Write answers only. Work across the page

A	44 ÷ 2 = 22	4·4 ÷ 2 = 2·2	0·44 ÷ 2 = 0·22	0·044 ÷ 2 = 0·022
B	12 ÷ 4 = 3	1·2 ÷ 4 = 0·3	0·12 ÷ 4 = 0·03	0·012 ÷ 4 = 0·003
C	15 ÷ 5 = 3	1·5 ÷ 5 = 0·3	0·15 ÷ 5 = 0·03	0·015 ÷ 5 = 0·003
D	4·2 ÷ 6 = 0·7	0·42 ÷ 6 = 0·07	0·042 ÷ 6 = 0·007	0·035 ÷ 7 = 0·005
E	2·4 ÷ 8 = 0·3	0·24 ÷ 8 = 0·03	0·024 ÷ 8 = 0·003	0·063 ÷ 9 = 0·007
F	0·56 ÷ 7 = 0·08	0·072 ÷ 9 = 0·008	0·1 ÷ 2 = 0·05	0·1 ÷ 5 = 0·02
G	1·08 ÷ 9 = 0·12	1·08 ÷ 12 = 0·09	0·209 ÷ 11 = 0·019	0·121 ÷ 11 = 0·011

Divide (÷)

H	$\begin{array}{r} 18 \\ 2\overline{)36} \end{array}$	$\begin{array}{r} 1\cdot8 \\ 2\overline{)3\cdot6} \end{array}$	$\begin{array}{r} 0\cdot18 \\ 2\overline{)0\cdot36} \end{array}$	$\begin{array}{r} 0\cdot15 \\ 3\overline{)0\cdot45} \end{array}$	$\begin{array}{r} 0\cdot15 \\ 5\overline{)0\cdot75} \end{array}$
I	$\begin{array}{r} 1\cdot42 \\ 4\overline{)5\cdot68} \end{array}$	$\begin{array}{r} 1\cdot34 \\ 6\overline{)8\cdot04} \end{array}$	$\begin{array}{r} 1\cdot29 \\ 7\overline{)9\cdot03} \end{array}$	$\begin{array}{r} 1\cdot15 \\ 9\overline{)10\cdot35} \end{array}$	$\begin{array}{r} 1\cdot18 \\ 8\overline{)9\cdot44} \end{array}$
J	$\begin{array}{r} 3\cdot3 \\ 5\overline{)16\cdot5} \end{array}$	$\begin{array}{r} 1\cdot5 \\ 7\overline{)10\cdot5} \end{array}$	$\begin{array}{r} 2\cdot34 \\ 6\overline{)14\cdot04} \end{array}$	$\begin{array}{r} 1\cdot26 \\ 8\overline{)10\cdot08} \end{array}$	$\begin{array}{r} 1\cdot55 \\ 11\overline{)17\cdot05} \end{array}$
K	$\begin{array}{r} 5\cdot2 \\ 3\overline{)15\cdot6} \end{array}$	$\begin{array}{r} 0\cdot52 \\ 3\overline{)1\cdot56} \end{array}$	$\begin{array}{r} 0\cdot42 \\ 4\overline{)1\cdot68} \end{array}$	$\begin{array}{r} 0\cdot24 \\ 6\overline{)1\cdot44} \end{array}$	$\begin{array}{r} 0\cdot47 \\ 5\overline{)2\cdot35} \end{array}$
L	$\begin{array}{r} 0\cdot44 \\ 4\overline{)1\cdot76} \end{array}$	$\begin{array}{r} 0\cdot044 \\ 4\overline{)0\cdot176} \end{array}$	$\begin{array}{r} 0\cdot041 \\ 5\overline{)0\cdot205} \end{array}$	$\begin{array}{r} 0\cdot047 \\ 7\overline{)0\cdot329} \end{array}$	$\begin{array}{r} 0\cdot054 \\ 8\overline{)0\cdot432} \end{array}$
M	$\begin{array}{r} 0\cdot27 \\ 5\overline{)1\cdot35} \end{array}$	$\begin{array}{r} 0\cdot101 \\ 7\overline{)0\cdot707} \end{array}$	$\begin{array}{r} 0\cdot012 \\ 9\overline{)0\cdot108} \end{array}$	$\begin{array}{r} 0\cdot091 \\ 11\overline{)1\cdot001} \end{array}$	$\begin{array}{r} 0\cdot092 \\ 12\overline{)1\cdot104} \end{array}$

DIVISION OF DECIMALS

Divide (÷)

A					
	0·2	0·29	0·119	0·032	0·058
	5)1·0	7)2·03	6)0·714	9)0·288	8)0·464

Change tenths remaining into hundredths to finish the answer

B					
	1·15	3·35	2·12	2·56	1·35
	2)2·3	4)13·4	5)10·6	5)12·8	8)10·8

C					
	0·35	6·14	2·05	5·05	4·05
	2)0·7	5)30·7	8)16·4	6)30·3	12)48·6

Change hundredths remaining into thousandths to finish the answer

D					
	3·225	0·655	1·175	1·255	1·608
	2)6·45	4)2·62	6)7·05	8)10·04	5)8·04

E					
	1·535	0·164	0·115	0·085	0·035
	4)6·14	5)0·82	8)0·92	6)0·51	12)0·42

Change tenths over into hundredths and hundredths over into thousandths to finish the answer

F					
	3·515	0·175	0·075	0·425	0·275
	2)7·03	4)0·7	8)0·6	8)3·4	12)3·3

Take answers to the third decimal place

G					
	9·725	0·234	0·524	0·455	0·096
	8)77·8	5)1·17	7)3·6	9)4·1	11)1·06

H					
	0·071	0·858	0·745	0·711	0·908
	6)0·43	7)6·01	11)8·2	9)6·4	12)10·9

Write answers only

A	$\frac{1}{2}$ hour = 30 minutes	$\frac{1}{4}$ minute = 15 seconds
B	45 minutes = $\frac{3}{4}$ hour	90 seconds = $1\frac{1}{2}$ minutes
C	a fortnight = 14 days	48 hours = 2 days
D	3 minutes = 180 seconds	3 days = 72 hours
E	26 weeks = $\frac{1}{2}$ year	75 minutes = $1\frac{1}{4}$ hours
F	August has 31 days	Feb. 1968 had 29 days

Add (+)

G

min.	sec.		hr.	min.		wk.	days		days	hr.
5	16		3	45		6	6		5	23
4	37			50		17	5			18
	23		7	9		9	6			9
2	58			38		28	4		3	21
13	14		12	22		63	0		10	23

Subtract (−)

H

min.	sec.		hr.	min.		wk.	days		days	hr.
15	10		6	23		5	4		3	17
− 9	18		−	56		− 3	6		− 2	21
5	52		5	27		1	5			20

Change to minutes

I 200 sec. — 3 min. 20 sec.; 307 sec. — 5 min. 7 sec.

Change to hours

J 275 min. — 4 hr. 35 sec.; 440 min. — 7 hr. 20 sec.

Change to days

K 77 hr. — 3 days 5 hr.; 103 hr. — 4 days 7 hr.; 176 hr. — 7 days 8 hr.; 235 hr. — 9 days 19 hr.

Change to weeks

L 50 days — 7 wk. 1 day; 87 days — 12 wk. 3 days; 106 days — 15 wk. 1 day; 249 days — 35 wk. 4 days

Multiply (×)

A	min. sec.	min. sec.	hr. min.	hr. min.	hr. min.
	2 34	1 57	2 23	3 37	2 56
×	5	9	6	11	8
	12 50	17 33	14 18	39 47	23 28

B	wk. days	wk. days	days hr.	days hr.	days hr.
	3 5	5 6	2 11	3 17	4 21
×	10	12	7	9	12
	37 1	70 2	17 5	33 9	58 12

Change to seconds

C	min. sec.	min. sec.
	3 18	5 48
	198	348

Change to minutes

D	hr. min.	hr. min.
	4 37	6 56
	277	416

Change to hours

E	days hr.	days hr.	days hr.	days hr.
	2 16	4 19	3 23	7 18
	64	115	95	186

Change to days

F	wk. days	wk. days	wk. days	wk. days
	2 4	5 6	7 5	10 6
	18	41	54	76

Divide (÷)

G	min. sec.	min. sec.	hr. min.	hr. min.
	1 23	56	31 r1 min.	1 53
	6)8 18	5)4 40	7)3 38	9)16 57

H	hr. min.	wk. days	wk. days	days hr.
	54	1 3	5 r9 days	1 5
	11)9 54	10)14 2	12)9 6	8)9 16

I	days hr.	days hr.	days hr.	days hr.
	19	1 15	23 r5 hr.	1 18
	7)5 13	9)14 15	11)10 18	12)21 0

THIRDS $\frac{1}{3}$ and SIXTHS $\frac{1}{6}$

Work across the page

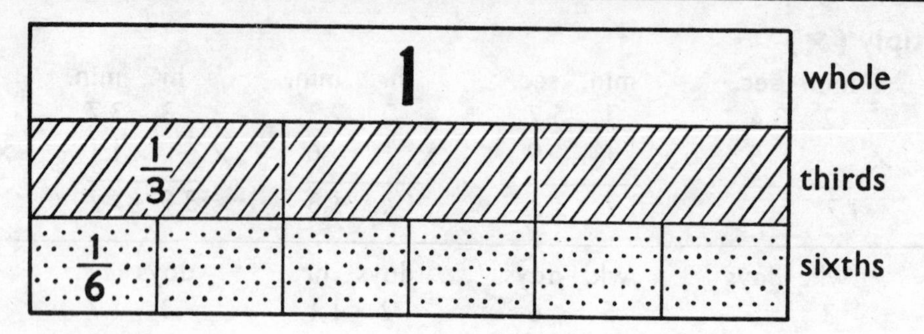

What are the missing figures?

A	$1=\frac{3}{3}$	$\frac{1}{3}=\frac{2}{6}$	$1=\frac{6}{6}$	$\frac{2}{6}=\frac{1}{3}$
B	$\frac{4}{6}=\frac{2}{3}$	$\frac{1}{6}+\frac{1}{6}=\frac{1}{3}$	$\frac{1}{3}+\frac{2}{3}=1$	$\frac{2}{6}+\frac{2}{6}=\frac{2}{3}$
C	$1-\frac{1}{3}=\frac{2}{3}$	$1-\frac{2}{3}=\frac{1}{3}$	$\frac{1}{3}-\frac{1}{6}=\frac{1}{6}$	$\frac{2}{3}-\frac{1}{6}=\frac{3}{6}$
D	$\frac{3}{6}+\frac{1}{6}=\frac{2}{3}$	$1-\frac{3}{6}=\frac{3}{6}$ or $\frac{1}{2}$	$\frac{1}{3}+\frac{1}{6}=\frac{3}{6}$	$\frac{2}{3}-\frac{3}{6}=\frac{1}{6}$

Write how many there are

E thirds in 1, 3 2, 6 $1\frac{1}{3}$, 4 $2\frac{1}{3}$, 7 $3\frac{2}{3}$, 11 4, 12 $5\frac{2}{3}$, 17

F sixths in $\frac{2}{3}$, 4 $1\frac{1}{6}$, 7 $1\frac{1}{3}$, 8 $1\frac{2}{3}$, 10 $2\frac{1}{6}$, 13 3, 18 $1\frac{5}{6}$, 11
$2\frac{1}{3}$, 14 $3\frac{1}{3}$, 20 $2\frac{5}{6}$, 17 $3\frac{2}{3}$, 22 $4\frac{1}{6}$, 25 $5\frac{1}{3}$, 32 $4\frac{2}{3}$ 28

Which is bigger?

G $\frac{1}{3}$ or $\frac{1}{6}$ $\frac{1}{3}$ $\frac{1}{3}$ or $\frac{3}{6}$ $\frac{3}{6}$ $\frac{2}{3}$ or $\frac{3}{6}$ $\frac{2}{3}$ $\frac{2}{3}$ or $\frac{5}{6}$ $\frac{5}{6}$ $1\frac{1}{3}$ or $1\frac{1}{6}$ $1\frac{1}{3}$

If possible write answers only

H	$\frac{1}{3}$ of 6p = 2p	$\frac{1}{3}$ of 9p = 3p	$\frac{1}{3}$ of 12 kg = 4 kg	$\frac{1}{3}$ of 1 min. = 20 sec.
I	$\frac{2}{3}$ of 6p = 4p	$\frac{2}{3}$ of 9p = 6p	$\frac{2}{3}$ of 12p = 8p	$\frac{2}{3}$ of 1 hr. = 40 min.
J	$\frac{1}{6}$ of 6p = 1p	$\frac{5}{6}$ of 6p = 5p	$\frac{1}{6}$ of 18 m = 3 m	$\frac{5}{6}$ of 18 m = 15 m
K	$\frac{1}{6}$ of 3p = $\frac{1}{2}$p	$\frac{5}{6}$ of 3p = $2\frac{1}{2}$p	$\frac{5}{6}$ of 9p = $7\frac{1}{2}$p	$\frac{5}{6}$ of 12 hr. = 10 hr.

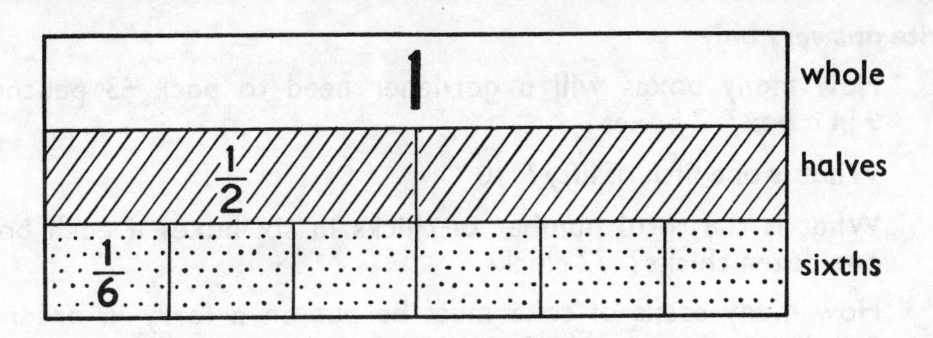

What are the missing figures?

A $1=\frac{2}{2}$ $\frac{1}{2}=\frac{3}{6}$ $\frac{1}{2}-\frac{1}{6}=\frac{2}{6}$ $\frac{1}{2}-\frac{2}{6}=\frac{1}{6}$

B $\frac{1}{6}+\frac{1}{6}=\frac{2}{6}=\frac{1}{3}$ $\frac{2}{6}+\frac{1}{6}=\frac{3}{6}=\frac{1}{2}$

C $1-\frac{1}{2}=\frac{1}{2}$ $1-\frac{1}{6}=\frac{5}{6}$ $1-\frac{3}{6}=\frac{3}{6}$ or $\frac{1}{2}$ $1-\frac{5}{6}=\frac{1}{6}$

Write how many there are

D halves in 1, 2 2, 4 $1\frac{1}{2}$, 3 $2\frac{1}{2}$, 5 $3\frac{1}{2}$, 7 $7\frac{1}{2}$, 15 9, 18

E sixths in $\frac{1}{2}$, 3 $1\frac{1}{2}$, 9 $\frac{1}{3}$, 2 2, 12 $2\frac{1}{3}$, 14 $2\frac{1}{2}$, 15 $3\frac{1}{2}$, 21

Which is bigger?

F $\frac{1}{2}$ or $\frac{1}{6}$ $\frac{1}{2}$ $\frac{1}{2}$ or $\frac{2}{6}$ $\frac{1}{2}$ $\frac{1}{2}$ or $\frac{1}{3}$ $\frac{1}{2}$ $\frac{1}{2}$ or $\frac{5}{6}$ $\frac{5}{6}$ 1 or $\frac{7}{6}$ $\frac{7}{6}$

Put in order of size—biggest first

G $\frac{1}{6}, \frac{1}{2}, \frac{1}{3}$ $\frac{1}{2}, \frac{1}{3}, \frac{1}{6}$ $\frac{5}{6}, \frac{2}{3}, \frac{1}{2}$ $\frac{5}{6}, \frac{2}{3}, \frac{1}{2}$ $\frac{2}{3}, \frac{1}{2}, 1$ $1, \frac{2}{3}, \frac{1}{2}$

$\frac{5}{6}, 1\frac{1}{3}, 1\frac{1}{2}$ $1\frac{1}{2}, 1\frac{1}{3}, \frac{5}{6}$ $1\frac{1}{6}, 1\frac{1}{2}, 1\frac{1}{3}$ $1\frac{1}{2}, 1\frac{1}{3}, 1\frac{1}{6}$

Work out these in your book

H What must be added to one half to make a whole one? one half

I What is one half of one third? $\frac{1}{6}$

J What must be added to one third to make one half? $\frac{1}{6}$

K What must be added to one half to make five sixths? $\frac{2}{6}$ or $\frac{1}{3}$

L What must be added to one half to make two thirds? $\frac{1}{6}$

M What is one third of one half? $\frac{1}{6}$

N What is one third of one hour in minutes? 20 minutes

O How many centimetres are there in one and a half metres? 150

Write answers only

A How many boxes will a gardener need to pack 63 peaches, putting 9 in a box? 7 boxes

B What is one fifth of fifty? 10

C What is the total number of chicks in six boxes if each box contains one dozen chicks? 72 chicks

D How many sacks of coke must be put on a lorry in order to deliver 8 sacks of coke to each of nine houses? 72 sacks

E A lorry can carry five tons. How many journeys must it make to remove sixty tons of bricks? 12 journeys

F Each of seven pupils is carrying eleven books. How many books are there altogether? 77 books

G From a ball of string nine pieces, each ten metres long, are cut. What is the total length used? 90 metres

H One hundred tulips are to be put into bunches of ten. How many bunches will there be? 10 bunches

Work out these sums in your book

I It has been arranged for six 'buses to take 330 pupils on a school outing. How many will there be to each 'bus? 55 pupils

J A gardener wishes to plant 7 rows of bulbs with 45 in each row. How many bulbs must he order? 315 bulbs

K A machine makes two-hundred-and-fifty-six bricks per hour. How many does it make in a day of eight working hours? 2 048 bricks

L A packer has 9 crates into which he must pack 432 cauliflowers. How many should he put into each crate? 48 cauliflowers

M How many tables will be needed to seat four-hundred-and-fifty pupils with room for 12 at each table? 38 tables

N How many boxes, each holding 12 tennis balls, can be filled from 700 tennis balls? 58 boxes

O Find how many $\frac{1}{2}$ litre bottles of milk can be filled from 75 litres of milk. 150 bottles

Divide (÷)

A

20)40 = 2	20)60 = 3	20)80 = 4	30)60 = 2	40)80 = 2

B

21)42 = 2	21)63 = 3	21)84 = 4	31)62 = 2	41)82 = 2

C

22)44 = 2	22)66 = 3	20)41 = 2r1	20)61 = 3r1	21)43 = 2r1

D

30)63 = 2r3	21)67 = 3r4	22)46 = 2r2	31)68 = 2r6	22)90 = 4r2

E

21)50 = 2r8	21)71 = 3r8	31)71 = 2r9	20)47 = 2r7	23)50 = 2r4

F

20)100 = 5	30)120 = 4	50)150 = 3	30)150 = 5	20)140 = 7

G

20)220 = 11	21)231 = 11	21)252 = 12	20)420 = 21	31)651 = 21

H

21)483 = 23	22)704 = 32	31)372 = 12	23)736 = 32	32)416 = 13

A–E Single figure quotients, with remainders in **C–E**.
F–H Divisor not contained in first two figures of dividend and no remainders.

Divide (÷)

A	21)210 (10)	20)400 (20)	30)6003 (200r3)	40)8406 (210r6)
B	31)6820 (220)	32)7042 (220r2)	21)4644 (221r3)	21)2228 (106r2)
C	22)5060 (230)	31)6300 (203r7)	23)2420 (105r5)	22)4510 (205)
D	19)437 (23)	29)1220 (42r2)	18)1908 (106)	28)1182 (42r6)
E	18)3654 (203)	17)5204 (306r2)	27)2810 (104r2)	38)7760 (204r8)

Work out these in your book

F A motorist found that on a journey of 756 kilometres he had used 63 litres of petrol. How many km had he travelled for each litre of petrol used? 12 km

G A bricklayer laid 2 160 bricks during 18 working hours. How many would that be for each working hour? 120 bricks

A–B introduce more difficult examples having noughts in answers.

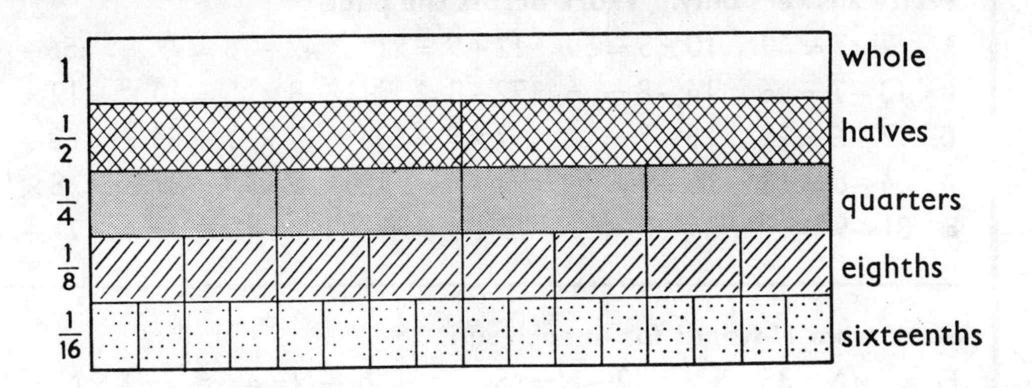

Which is the bigger number?

A $\frac{1}{2}$ or $\frac{1}{4}$ $\frac{1}{2}$ | $\frac{1}{2}$ or $\frac{1}{8}$ $\frac{1}{2}$ | $\frac{1}{16}$ or $\frac{1}{4}$ $\frac{1}{4}$ | $\frac{1}{8}$ or $\frac{1}{4}$ $\frac{1}{4}$

B $\frac{1}{8}$ or $\frac{3}{16}$ $\frac{3}{16}$ | $\frac{1}{4}$ or $\frac{3}{16}$ $\frac{1}{4}$ | $\frac{1}{4}$ or $\frac{3}{8}$ $\frac{3}{8}$ | $\frac{1}{2}$ or $\frac{3}{4}$ $\frac{3}{4}$

C $\frac{3}{8}$ or $\frac{5}{16}$ $\frac{3}{8}$ | $\frac{1}{2}$ or $\frac{9}{16}$ $\frac{9}{16}$ | $\frac{3}{4}$ or $\frac{5}{8}$ $\frac{3}{4}$ | $\frac{7}{8}$ or $\frac{11}{16}$ $\frac{7}{8}$

What are the missing figures? Use the diagram

D $\frac{1}{2}=\frac{2}{4}=\frac{4}{8}=\frac{8}{16}$ | $1=\frac{4}{4}=\frac{16}{16}=\frac{2}{2}$

E $\frac{1}{2}=\frac{1}{4}+\frac{1}{4}$ | $\frac{1}{2}=\frac{1}{4}+\frac{2}{8}$ | $\frac{3}{8}+\frac{1}{8}=\frac{2}{4}$

F $\frac{3}{8}+\frac{1}{8}=\frac{1}{2}$ | $\frac{1}{16}+\frac{1}{16}=\frac{1}{8}$ | $\frac{1}{16}+\frac{3}{16}=\frac{1}{4}$

G $\frac{1}{4}=\frac{1}{8}+\frac{1}{8}$ | $\frac{5}{16}=\frac{1}{4}+\frac{1}{16}$ | $\frac{1}{8}=\frac{1}{16}+\frac{1}{16}$

H $\frac{3}{16}=\frac{1}{8}+\frac{1}{16}$ | $\frac{3}{8}=\frac{1}{4}+\frac{1}{8}$ | $\frac{3}{4}=\frac{1}{2}+\frac{1}{4}$

I $\frac{1}{2}=\frac{4}{8}$ | $\frac{1}{4}=\frac{4}{16}$ | $\frac{1}{8}=\frac{2}{16}$ | $\frac{1}{2}=\frac{2}{4}$

J $\frac{3}{4}=\frac{6}{8}$ | $\frac{3}{4}=\frac{12}{16}$ | $\frac{3}{8}=\frac{6}{16}$ | $\frac{7}{8}=\frac{14}{16}$

K $1-\frac{1}{2}=\frac{1}{2}$ | $1-\frac{1}{4}=\frac{3}{4}$ | $\frac{1}{2}-\frac{1}{4}=\frac{1}{4}$ | $\frac{1}{4}-\frac{1}{8}=\frac{1}{8}$

L $1-\frac{3}{4}=\frac{1}{4}$ | $1-\frac{5}{8}=\frac{3}{8}$ | $1-\frac{9}{16}=\frac{7}{16}$ | $\frac{1}{2}-\frac{3}{16}=\frac{5}{16}$

Put in order of size—biggest first

M $\frac{1}{8}, \frac{1}{2}, \frac{1}{4}$ $\frac{1}{2}, \frac{1}{4}, \frac{1}{8}$ | $\frac{1}{8}, \frac{1}{2}, \frac{3}{16}$ $\frac{1}{2}, \frac{3}{16}, \frac{1}{8}$ | $\frac{1}{2}, 1, \frac{1}{4}$ $1, \frac{1}{2}, \frac{1}{4}$ | $1\frac{1}{2}, 1\frac{1}{16}, 1\frac{1}{8}$ $1\frac{1}{2}, 1\frac{1}{8}, 1\frac{1}{16}$

N $\frac{1}{4}, \frac{1}{3}, \frac{1}{2}$ $\frac{1}{2}, \frac{1}{3}, \frac{1}{4}$ | $\frac{3}{8}, \frac{1}{2}, \frac{3}{4}$ $\frac{3}{4}, \frac{1}{2}, \frac{3}{8}$ | $1\frac{9}{16}, \frac{3}{4}, 1\frac{1}{2}$ $1\frac{9}{16}, 1\frac{1}{2}, \frac{3}{4}$ | $\frac{1}{6}, \frac{1}{3}, \frac{1}{4}$ $\frac{1}{3}, \frac{1}{4}, \frac{1}{6}$

GENERAL REVISION

Write answers only. Work across the page

A	7×7 = 49	10×5 = 50	12+9 = 21	42÷ 6 = 7	56÷ 7 = 8
B	13−7 = 6	14−8 = 6	72÷8 = 9	8× 5 = 40	12× 6 = 72
C	17+6 = 23	15−7 = 8	7×9 = 63	12× 7 = 84	63÷ 9 = 7
D	64÷8 = 8	16+9 = 25	72÷8 = 9	9× 9 = 81	8×12 = 96
E	81÷9 = 9	84÷7 = 12	23+8 = 31	100÷12 = 8 r 4	21 − 8 = 13

State what *N* stands for in each sum

F	$7 \times N = 35$ 5	$12 - N = 5$ 7	$24 \div N = 4$ 6	$8 \times N = 56$ 7
G	$54 \div N = 6$ 9	$13 + N = 22$ 9	$63 \div N = 7$ 9	$9 \times N = 108$ 12

State the place value of the figure 7 in each of these numbers

H 2 704 hundreds — 37·26 units

I 5·607 thousandths — 290·7 tenths

Write these numbers in figures

J three hundred and seven 307 — four thousand and nine 4 009

K five and four tenths 5·4 — one unit, and four hundredths 1·04

L six units and seventeen thousandths 6·017

M ninety and seven tenths 90·7

State how many tenths in

N 0·6 6 — 1·3 13 — 2·06 20 — 3·17 31 — 10·8 108 — 0·07 0

State how many hundredths in

O 0·23 23 — 0·08 8 — 0·172 17 — 1·06 106 — 1·109 110 — 0·008 0

State how many thousandths in

P 0·004 4 — 0·037 37 — 0·106 106 — 0·01 10 — 0·23 230 — 0·109 109

GENERAL REVISION

Write in figures

A a quarter past eleven o'clock in the evening 11.15 p.m.

B the time three-quarters of an hour before mid-day 11.15 a.m.

C 3rd Feb. 1965 3.2.65 31st Oct. 1962 31.10.62 17th May 1970 17.5.70

Give the time 24 hours after

D 9 p.m. 7th August 9 p.m. 8th August

11.45 a.m. 30th June 11.45 a.m. 1st July

State how long it is from

E 11.35 a.m. to 1.10 p.m. 1 hr. 35 min.

9.30 p.m. to 7.50 a.m. 10 hr. 20 min.

F 10.45 a.m. Monday to 3.20 p.m. Tuesday. 28 hr. 35 min.

Add (+)

G

hr.	min.	min.	sec.	wk.	days	days	hr.	days	hr.
7	38	4	50	4	6	2	7	6	18
	56	2	8		5	3	12		22
3	9		47	3	6	1	5	5	9
11	43	7	45	9	3	7	0	13	1

Subtract (−)

H

wk.	days	days	hr.	days	hr.	min.	sec.	hr.	min.
10	5	3	10	13	8	20	5	7	34
− 3	6	− 2	15	− 5	19	− 18	43	− 4	57
6	6		19	7	13	1	22	2	37

Multiply (×)

I

wk.	days	days	hr.	days	hr.	min.	sec.	hr.	min.
13	6	3	6	2	17	3	15	1	34
×	5	×	6	×	8	×	9	×	14
69	2	19	12	21	16	29	15	17	14

Divide (÷)

J

wk.	days	days	hr.	days	hr.	min.	sec.	hr.	min.
1	3	0	8	1	10	1	15	0	$27\frac{1}{2}$
9) 12	6	7) 2	8	9) 12	18	8) 10	0	12) 5	30

GENERAL REVISION

Work across the page

Add (+)

A

3765	4839	$52\frac{1}{2}$p	£6·37	1·07 cm	3·074 kl
408	78	$8\frac{1}{2}$p	£0·86	12·6 cm	0·89 kl
6974	650	70 p	£9·05	4·9 cm	7·6 kl
5089	947	$19\frac{1}{2}$p	£7·48	14·85 cm	0·769 kl
16236	6514	$150\frac{1}{2}$p	£23·76	33·42 cm	12·333 kl

Subtract (−)

B

4006	8903	$70\frac{1}{2}$p	£3·05	7·63 l	2·08 km
− 3908	− 5994	− $38\frac{1}{2}$p	− £0·$68\frac{1}{2}$	− 0·95 l	− 0·904 km
98	2909	32 p	£2·$36\frac{1}{2}$	6·68 l	1·176 km

Multiply (×)

C

305	4089	$27\frac{1}{2}$p	£0·$67\frac{1}{2}$	£2·$06\frac{1}{2}$	0·609 m
× 8	× 12	× 9	× 11	× 12	× 12
2440	49056	$247\frac{1}{2}$p	£7·$42\frac{1}{2}$	£24·78	7·308 m

Divide (÷)

D

9)816	7)5096	12)8500	8)£9·76	11)£13·53
90 r 6	728	708 r 4	£1·22	£1·23

E

5)$84\frac{1}{2}$p	7)$96\frac{1}{2}$p	9)£11·77	11)£5·60	12)£13·$50\frac{1}{2}$
$16\frac{1}{2}$p r 2p	$13\frac{1}{2}$p r 2p	£1·$30\frac{1}{2}$ r $2\frac{1}{2}$p	£0·$50\frac{1}{2}$ r $4\frac{1}{2}$p	£1·$12\frac{1}{2}$ r $\frac{1}{2}$p

F

6)8·022	9)9·288	8)24·4	12)2·1	8)0·76
1·337	1·032	3·05	0·175	0·095

Multiply (×)

G

247	608	750
× 23	× 35	× 18
5681	21280	13500

Divide (÷)

H

31)744	29)754
24	26

GENERAL REVISION

Write in columns and add. Work across the page

A	3·7 m + 0·86 m + 12·7 m 17·26 m	$16\frac{1}{2}$p + $9\frac{1}{2}$p + $80\frac{1}{2}$p $106\frac{1}{2}$p
B	£10·70 + £0·85$\frac{1}{2}$ + £3·09 £14·64$\frac{1}{2}$	£7·63$\frac{1}{2}$ + £0·84$\frac{1}{2}$ + £0·09$\frac{1}{2}$ £8·57$\frac{1}{2}$

Write in columns and subtract

C	£10 − £3·24$\frac{1}{2}$ £6·75$\frac{1}{2}$	£5 − 63$\frac{1}{2}$p £4·36$\frac{1}{2}$	4·07 l − 0·674 l 3·396 l

Complete

D	0·627 l = 627 ml	0·803 g = 803 mg	1·078 m = 1 078 mm
E	0·083 m = 83 mm	7·62 g = 7 620 mg	2·08 l = 2 080 ml
F	0·04 m = 40 mm	0·5 g = 500 mg	1·5 l = 1 500 ml
G	2·7 g = 2 700 mg	1·08 l = 1 080 ml	0·09 m = 90 mm
H	1·009 l = 1 009 ml	0·007 m = 7 mm	0·6 m = 600 mm

Write as decimals in metres, litres or grammes

I	1 m 27 cm = 1·27 m	2 m 304 mm = 2·304 m	1 m 8 cm = 1·08 m
J	2 l 470 ml = 2·47 l	3 g 500 mg = 3·5 g	2 g 250 mg = 2·25 g
K	3 m 85 cm = 3·85 m	3 m 75 mm = 3·075 m	1 l 750 ml = 1·75 l
L	2 g 90 mg = 2·09 g	5 l 800 ml = 5·8 l	3 m 80 cm = 3·8 m
M	4 l 8 ml = 4·008 l	7 m 6 cm = 7·06 m	10 g 90 mg = 10·09 g

Complete

N	1·62 m = 1 m 62 cm	1·326 m = 1 m 326 mm	1·62 m = 1 m 620 mm
O	2·085 l = 2 l 85 ml	7·5 g = 7 g 500 mg	5·06 g = 5 g 60 mg
P	1·627 l = 1 l 627 ml	1·36 m = 1 m 36 cm	3·7 m = 3 m 70 cm
Q	3·08 g = 3 g 80 mg	2·6 g = 2 g 600 mg	4·09 l = 4 l 90 ml
R	2·4 m = 2 m 40 cm	1·3 m = 1 m 300 mm	2·063 g = 2 g 63 mg
S	4·07 l = 4 l 70 ml	3·96 l = 3 l 960 ml	5·8 m = 5 m 80 cm

GENERAL REVISION

Complete

A $\frac{1}{4}$ of 16hr. = 4hr. $\frac{2}{5}$ of 30min. = 12min. $\frac{3}{5}$ of $\frac{1}{2}$ metre = 30cm. (0·3 m)

B $\frac{5}{6}$ of 3 litre = 2·5 l $\frac{3}{8}$ of £1 = 37$\frac{1}{2}$p $\frac{3}{4}$ of 1 kilogramme = 750 g

C

$\frac{1}{4}$ kg of boiled ham @ £1·06 per kg	=	26$\frac{1}{2}$p
$\frac{3}{4}$ kg of bacon @ 46p per kg	=	34$\frac{1}{2}$p
$\frac{1}{4}$ kg of pressed beef @ 26p per $\frac{1}{2}$ kg	=	13p
9 eggs @ 1$\frac{1}{2}$p each	=	13$\frac{1}{2}$p
total	=	87$\frac{1}{2}$p or £0·87$\frac{1}{2}$

Work in your book

D Find the change from £1 when paying the bill in C. 12$\frac{1}{2}$p

E What must be added to 37·8 metres to increase the length of a rope to 50 metres? 12·2 m

F What is the maximum number of people who can be seated in a theatre having 72 seats in each of 25 rows? 1 800

G If a bottle of school milk contains 200 ml, what quantity of milk is needed to supply the school with 345 bottles each day during the school week—Monday to Friday? 345 l

H A car should travel 56 kilometres on 10 litres of petrol. How many litres should be needed on a tour of 980 kilometres? 175 l

I How long should you be away from home if you live a twenty minute journey from the station, catch a train at 10.15 and return by a train which should arrive at 16.50? 7 hrs. 15 mins.

J If hymn books are 17$\frac{1}{2}$p each, find how many can be bought for £17·50. 100

K Draw a right angle triangle so that, of the two sides which are perpendicular to each other, one is 12 cm and the other is 9 cm. What is the length of the third side? 15 cm

L Ann noticed that on the first day she read $\frac{2}{5}$ of the pages in a book and $\frac{1}{3}$ on the second day. If the book contained 240 pages how many pages were left for the third day? 64

NOTES TO THE TEACHER

Enthusiasm often swamps the best of intentions, even those of really conscientious teachers. It is essential to remember at all times that the pupil cannot fit the book. It is the teachers' task to fit the book to the pupil, and this is done often by the discreet use of the blackboard and oral questions and dictation. Throughout the book, where possible, new material is introduced by examples which revise previous steps in the topic, but the economic production of a book limits the amount of revisionary material which can be included, as well as the obvious fact that many pupils will require less than others. In the following pages notes have been included to help the teacher and a few typical examples of blackboard or dictation material are given. A wise teacher will do some blackboard work even with the most able pupils, especially in the early stages when a firm foundation must be laid.

As an example, by writing down on the blackboard or dictating the times arranged against letters A–C on page 80, the teacher can discover what has been retained from the previous class and what must be re-taught before proceeding with page 19.

It is assumed that experience (often referred to as the "Best Teacher") is keeping ahead of written work under the skilled guidance of the teacher, and it is suggested that at appropriate times the practical work will include many exercises which an author would like to include but cannot owing to changes in price and value, local conditions and customs, school facilities, etc., such as references to local industrial productions, local agricultural and horticultural productions, postage on letters, parcels, periodicals and newspapers, telephone and telegram charges with special rates, etc.

Before page 12:

The new decimal coinage simplifies many processes in handling quantities of mone
but it also imposes new disciplines. Numbers to 12 and to 20 are now extended int
one range—up to 100. Shopping will demand the addition of two or more quantitie
in the number range from 1 to 99, so composition of numbers in that range should b
well understood.

At each stage on this page the teacher should check that the pupil is well practised i
that stage before proceeding to the next. More, rather than less, practice would b
most advantageous.

Before page 14:

So far as subtraction of money is concerned when cash is involved, the values of coin
control the process. In paying for an article worth 27p the change will involve eithe
30−27 or 50−27, for if more than the equivalent of three tens were tendered the shop
keeper would automatically return the excess. Similarly, payment for an article wort
63p would involve 65−63, 70−63 or 100−63.

Before attempting this page the pupil should be given practice in arranging coins o
writing the equivalents that make up specific amounts, as

40p=4 tens or 3 tens+2 fives, etc.
65p=a fifty+a ten+1 five or 6 tens+1 five, etc.

encouraging the pupil to make as many alternatives as are reasonable.

Before page 19:

These exercises can be used as a check to ensure that the pupils are thoroughl
conversant with telling time in preparation for pages 19 and 20.

Draw clock faces showing these times

A	a quarter past ten	15 minutes past 7	3.15
B	half-past eleven	half-past eight	4.30
C	a quarter to two	15 minutes to 9	5.45

Before page 24:

Show on blackboard

24=3×8 8×3 6×4 4×6 2×12 12×2
24=2 dozens 24 hr.=1 day 24 mm=2·4 cm
24 cm=240 mm $24\times\frac{1}{2}$p=12p 24p=£0·24

Ask pupils to see how many items they can find for these numbers:

18 36 37 40 48 53 60 50 72

Before page 35:

Division of money has been included before decimal number because of the deviation from the general rule of decimals. In money we have two figures only after the decimal point, then, if necessary the fraction one half. Any remainders will be stated as pence.

Before page 42:

A pupil's mental alertness can often be sharpened by such exercises as

A	2+2+2=6	2×2×2=8	(2×2)+2=6
B	2×(2+2)=8	2+(2−2)=2	2×(2−2)=0
C	2+0+2=4	2×(2+0)=4	2×2×0=0
D	(2×2)−2=2	(2+2)−2=2	(2−2)×2=0
E	Arrange three figure twos to equal 24	22+2	
F	Arrange three figure fours to equal 40	44−4	

Before page 46:

Continued development of metric measures depends so much upon a thorough understanding of number values. Constant practice is required to develop facility in converting from one measure to another, from a multiple to a unit, or from a unit to a submultiple. The operation of expressing litres as kilolitres is a direct parallel to expressing millilitres as litres, but the relative values of one to the other must be well understood and maintained.

It is not sufficient to know that to multiply by a thousand we move the figures three places to left, but the pupil must know and understand that in

4 926

there are four thousands
forty-nine hundreds
four hundred and ninety-two tens
and four thousand nine hundred and twenty-six units.

The same pupil must also know and understand that in

3·765

there are three units
thirty-seven tenths
three hundred and seventy-six hundredths
and three thousand seven hundred and sixty-five thousandths.

This knowledge will be built up in gradual steps and with much revision.

Before page 60:

82 **Some oral or written revision of time may be of benefit to some pupils.**

Write in figures the time

A fifteen minutes past seven o'clock in the morning. 7.15 a.m.

B ten minutes to six o'clock in the evening. 5.50 p.m.

C a half-hour before mid-day. 11.30 a.m.

D two and a half hours after mid-day. 2.30 p.m.

E twenty-five minutes to twelve o'clock midnight. 11.35 p.m.

F thirty-seven minutes past twelve o'clock midnight. 12.37 a.m.

G one and a half hours after twelve o'clock midnight. 1.30 a.m.

Give the time 24 hours after

H 8 a.m. 5th May 8 a.m. 6th May 5.15 p.m. 1st June 5.15 p.m. 2nd June

I 2 p.m. 31st May 2 p.m. 1st June 3.05 a.m. 30th April 3.05 a.m. 1st May

J 11.55 p.m. 28th February 1971 11.55 p.m. 1st March 1971

Give the time 24 hours before

K Noon 8th April Noon 7th April 9 p.m. 11th June 9 p.m. 10th June

L 1 a.m. 30th May 1 a.m. 29th May 5 a.m. 1st June 5 a.m. 31st May

M 12 o'clock midnight Wednesday 12 o'clock midnight Tuesday

N 12 o'clock noon 1st March 1972 12 o'clock noon 29th Feb. 1972

Say which month comes after

O Feb. Mar. June July Aug. Sept. Oct. Nov. Dec. Jan.

Say which month comes before

P Oct. Sept. Apr. Mar. Jan. Dec. May Apr. Nov. Oct.

Name the month which is three months after

Q Jan. Apr. Feb. May Aug. Nov. Apr. July Sept. Dec.

R Nov. 1970 Feb. 1971 Dec. 1974 Mar. 1975 Oct. 1973 Jan. 1974

If 27th August was on Friday give the date of

S the following Sunday 29th Aug. the following Friday 3rd Sept.

T the following Wednesday 1st Sept. the previous Tuesday 24th Aug.

U the previous Friday 20th Aug. the previous Monday week 16th Aug.

Say how long it is from

V 9.15 p.m. to 3.45 a.m. 6 hr. 30 min. 8.50 a.m. to 1.25 p.m. 4 hr 35 min.

W 10.11.72 to 5.2.73 87 days May '72 to Sept. '74 2 yr. 4 mth.